LANGUAGE OF GOD

Level F

Sandra Garant

Sandra Garant is a veteran homeschooling mom, business writer, and attorney. She taught her three children at home until they were ready for college. She has written several books, including the *It's a Mystery* series of children's retreats and *Creative Communications: Thirty Writing, Speaking, and Drawing Projects for Homeschoolers*. She is married to George Garant, and they live happily in San Antonio, TX. Sandra attends Our Lady of the Atonement Church. She is a member of the San Antonio Chesterton Society and the Catholic Lawyers Guild of San Antonio.

ISBN: 978-0-9824585-1-8

For more information, see:

www.chcweb.com

Or contact:

Catholic Heritage Curricula
P.O. Box 579090
Modesto, CA 95357

Printed by Sheridan Books, Inc.
Chelsea, Michigan
August 2015
Print code: 374557

Cover photo credit: Comstock.com

To my sterling friends

Donna Kessler and Pat DeVillez

TABLE OF CONTENTS

I. Parts of Speech, *1–86*

2   **Subjects**
3   **Predicates**
4   **Subjects and Predicates in Questions**
       Predicates in Questions Exercise
6   **The Independent Clause**
       Independent Clauses or Not Exercise
       Understood Subjects Exercise
       Review of Subjects and Predicates
11   **Simple and Compound Sentences**
       Mixing Simple and Compound
       Sentences Exercise
       Compound Subjects Exercise
       Compound Predicates Exercise
16   **Nouns**
16   **Compound Nouns**
       Forming More Compound Nouns
       Exercise
19   **Compound Words**
       Hyphenated Compound Noun Exercise
       More Compound Nouns Exercise
       Review of Compound Sentences
23   **Possessive Nouns**
24   **Plural Names**
25   **Plural Possessive Nouns**
       Singular and Plural Possessive Nouns
       Exercise
       Writing Possessive Nouns Exercise
28   **Collective Nouns**
       Matching Collective Nouns and
       Members Exercise
       Creating Collective Nouns Exercise
31   **Appositives**
       Appositive or Not Exercise
       Writing Appositives Exercise
       Review of Nouns

35   **Verbs**
36   **Linking a Subject and a Noun**
       Linking Verb or Not Exercise
       Another Linking Verb Exercise
39   **Action Verbs**
40   **Helping Verbs**
42   **Contracted Helping Verbs**
       Review of Verbs
44   **Verb Tenses**
       Writing Verb Tenses Exercise
46   **Progressive Verbs**
       Finding Past Progressive Verbs Exercise
       Writing Future Progressive Verbs
       Exercise
       Past, Present, or Future Progressive
       Exercise
50   **Irregular Verbs**
       Completing the Verb Forms Exercise
       Irregular and Regular Verbs Exercise
       Review of Verb Tenses
55   **Transitive Verbs**
       Writing Transitive Verbs Exercise
57   **Intransitive Verbs**
       Transitive or Intransitive Exercise
       Review of Verbs
60   **Pronouns**
61   **Personal Pronouns**
       Choosing Objective Singular and Plural
       Pronouns Exercise
       Choosing Possessive Singular and Plural
       Pronouns Exercise
65   **Indefinite Pronouns**
66   **Reflexive and Intensive Pronouns**
       Distinguishing between Reflexive and
       Intensive Pronouns Exercise
69   **Interrogative Pronouns**
       Review of Pronouns

72 **Adjectives**
Finding Adjectives Exercise

74 **Adverbs**
Another Adverb Relationship Exercise
Review of Adjectives and Adverbs

78 **Prepositions**

79 **More Prepositions**
Finding Prepositions Exercise

81 **Conjunctions**
Finding Conjunctions Exercise

83 **Interjections**
Choosing Interjections Exercise
Review of Prepositions, Conjunctions
and Interjections

II. Usage, 87–112

88 **Complex Sentences**

89 **Subject-Verb Agreement**
Singular and Plural Verbs Exercise
Singular and Plural Subjects Exercise

93 **Collective Nouns**

94 **Indefinite Pronouns**
Review of Indefinite Pronouns
Review of Subject-Verb Agreement

98 **Troublesome Words**
Lie Chanting Exercise
Choosing Lay or Lie Exercise
More Chanting Exercises

102 **More Troublesome Words and How to Use
Them Properly**
Choosing Grammatically Correct Words
Exercise

107 **Diagramming Sentences**

109 **Predicate Nouns and Adjectives**

110 **Compound Subjects and Predicates**

III. Mechanics, 113–168

114 **Capitalization**
Capitalizing Exercise

117 **Commas**
Using Commas Correctly Exercise

119 **More Uses for Commas**

121 **Parenthetic Expressions and Restrictive
Clauses**

123 **Commas and Conjunctions**
Review of Commas

126 **Semicolons and Colons**

128 **More Colons**
Review of Semicolons and Colons

132 **Quotation Marks**

134 **Quotation Marks or Italics?**

136 **Apostrophes**
Adding Apostrophes Exercise

138 **Apostrophes and Ownership**
Possession Without Apostrophe
Exercise
Possessive Pronoun Exercise

142 **Apostrophes and Contractions**
Review of Quotation Marks, Italics, and
Apostrophes

145 **Hyphens**

147 **More Uses for Hyphens**
To Hyphenate or Not Exercise

150 **Dashes**

152 **Parentheses**

154 **Citations of Works**

156 **Abbreviations**
Understanding Abbreviations Exercise

159 **Latin Abbreviations**

161 **The Ampersand &**

162 **Writing Numbers**

164 **It's About Time**
Review of Dashes and Parentheses
Review of Abbreviations and Numbers

IV. Composition, *169–230*

170 **Attention**
    Lively Words
172 **Clichés**
    The Sound of Being Exercise
    To Be or Not To Be Exercise
174 **Sentence Variety**
    Writing Sentences Exercise
    Writing More Sentences Exercise
177 **The Effective Paragraph**
    Writing Topic Sentences Exercise
180 **Examples of Effective Paragraphs**
    Writing Effective Paragraphs Exercise
183 **Proofreading**
184 **Transitions**
    Using Transitions Exercise
188 **Essays: Pre-writing Stage**
190 **Why are You Writing This Essay?**
192 **Main Thesis**
    Proofreading for Punctuation Exercise
195 **Developing Your Point**
197 **A Cohesive Essay**
200 **Completing the Pre-writing**
    Research Exercise
202 **Drafting Stage**
    Drafting Exercise
203 **Revision Stage**
    Subject-Verb Agreement Proofreading
    Exercise
    Proofreading Your Revision Exercise
205 **Publishing and Presenting Your Essay**
206 **Reports**
    Proofreading Exercise
    More Sources Exercise

209 **Interviewing Sources**
    Interview Exercise
212 **Organizing Information**
212 **Drafting Your Report**
    Proofreading Exercise
214 **Revising Your Report**
    Revising Exercise
    Proofreading Exercise
    Presenting Your Report
217 **Responding to Literature**
    Poetry Comprehension Exercise
    Reading Further Exercise
    Reading "The Sparrow and the Hare"
220 **Writing about the Fable**
    Proofreading Exercise
    Writing about "The Sparrow and the
    Hare" Exercise
223 **Narrative Writing**
225 **Deciding the Series of Events**
    Choosing the Order of Events Exercise
    Proofreading Exercise
227 **Dialogue in a Story**
    Listening to a Scripted Dialogue
    Exercise
    Purpose of Dialogue Exercise
    Writing Dialogue Exercise
230 **Writing Your Story**

231 **Answer Key**

Simple and Compound Sentences

People are interesting because God created us to be unique. No two people are exactly the same. Even twins have their own opinions and preferences. Writers and speakers vary their sentences to keep their readers and listeners interested. When your writing and speech become monotonous, which means lacking in variety, then your readers and listeners may miss your meaning.

A simple sentence is an independent clause with a subject and a predicate.

                  Subject   Predicate

Example: Innocent Smith / climbed a tree.

A simple sentence may contain more than one subject and more than one predicate.

          Subject   Subject   Predicate   Predicate

Example: Fr. Brown and Flambeau / walked around the scene of the crime and discussed the clues.

Who are the two subjects? Fr. Brown and Flambeau are the subjects.
The two predicates are "walked around the scene of the crime" and "discussed the clues." However, the sentence has only one independent clause and is a simple sentence.

A compound sentence contains at least two independent clauses.

               This is the first independent clause.

Example: "An inconvenience is only an adventure wrongly considered; an adventure is an

This is the second independent clause.
inconvenience rightly considered." (G. K. Chesterton)

The independent clauses may be joined by a semicolon or colon, or more commonly by a comma and a conjunction.

              This is the first independent clause.   This is the second independent clause.

Example: "The wind blew and howled throughout the night, **and** the clouds raced southwards before it."

Very short independent clauses may be joined by a comma only.

            1st independent clause.   2nd independent clause.

Example: "Bring on the sun, bring on the fun."

SIMPLE OR COMPOUND EXERCISE

Write SS if the sentence or question is a simple sentence. Write CS if the sentence or question is a compound sentence.

Example: _CS_ Someone forgot to close the door, and something wild came inside.

1. _SS_ Listen to that racket!

2. _CS_ The whole house is shaking, and the windows are rattling.

3. _SS_ Do you think an elephant and a chimpanzee are tramping and swinging about in the kitchen?

4. _CS_ I don't know, but I'm going to see what's happening.

5. _CS_ We did not find an elephant in the kitchen, nor did we find a rhinoceros there.

6. _SS_ We found pots and pans and cooking spoons strewn about.

7. _CS_ The kitchen was a mess, and the back door was wide open.

8. _CS_ Who could have created such chaos, and had they heard us coming and sneaked out the back door?

9. _SS_ We heard another loud crash and ducked.

10. _CS_ When we looked about again, what did we see?

11. _CS_ Two raccoons were sitting at the sink; they seemed to be annoyed that we had invited ourselves to their party.

12. _CS_ Scoot, you varmints!

Mixing Simple and Compound Sentences Exercise

Combine some of these simple sentences together to create a mixture of simple and compound sentences in the story.

The raccoons scooted. Two blurs of black and gray streaked out through the kitchen door. And I closed it. My sister shook her head. We both sighed. This was one big mess. But that wasn't the whole problem. Our friends were coming over in thirty minutes. We had promised to make hotdogs for them. The hotdog package was ripped. Half the hotdogs were missing. Where were the hotdog buns? The catsup was lying on the floor. The bottle had shattered. Would we be able to keep our promise of hospitality to our friends?

PARTS OF SPEECH

Two blurs of black and grey streaked out through the door, as the raccoons scooted. I closed it my sister shook her head as we both sighed. This was a big mess, but that wasn't the problem. Our friends were coming over in thirty minutes. We promised them hotdogs, but the pacage was ripped and half the hotdogs were missing. The catsup was lying on the floor with the bottle shattered Would we be able to keep our promise of hospotality to our friends

Photocopying of these pages is a violation of copyright law.

13

Compound Subjects Exercise

Underline both complete subjects in these compound sentences and questions.

Example: <u>The laptop computer</u> is conveniently portable; <u>the handheld computer</u> is pocket-sized.

1. Sr. Marie is a religious sister; Fr. Thomas is a diocesan priest.

2. Have you ever climbed a mountain, and have you ever seen the sea?

3. The baked fish with tomato sauce that we made for our Lenten supper tasted delicious, but the lemon cake that was leftover from yesterday was dry.

4. The computer was running slowly, and so Miss Millie Manor called tech support to ask for assistance.

5. Who was knocking at the front door, and what did they want?

6. Because the day at the science fair had been long and exciting, Kelly and Samuel were exhausted; they fell asleep in the car on the way home.

Compound Predicates Exercise

Underline both complete predicates in these compound sentences and questions.

Example: Many pages in the Latin book <u>are torn</u>, but the Greek workbook <u>is immaculate</u>.

1. Who knows the answer, and who doesn't even understand the question?

2. Mr. Singer was listening to Amadeus; Mrs. Singer was listening to Johann.

3. We were not making mud pies all morning; we had to stop because we ran out of aluminum pie pans.

4. Should we go swimming, or would you rather play soccer today?

5. The cat is making an awful racket and seems irritated, yet the dog is happily barking and jumping

   about under the cat's tree.

Nouns

The book of Genesis tells us that Adam gave names to creatures. The names we give to persons, places, things, events, conditions, qualities, and ideas enable us to be precise when we speak and write. So everything has a name. We even name the different parts of speech and then divide each part of speech again to describe its precise function.

Let's look at different types of nouns and their functions. If you completed Level E of this series, you studied common and proper nouns. Remember that common nouns refer to general names and that proper nouns refer to specific people, places, and things.

Example: Our priest (common noun) is Fr. James Michaels (proper noun).

We can divide proper and common nouns into further groups—compound nouns, possessive nouns, collective nouns, and appositives.

Compound Nouns

We call nouns that are made up of two or more words compound nouns. All the words in a compound noun do not have to be nouns, as you can see in the following chart:

Noun + Noun	godparents	one word
Noun + Verb	homeschooling home-schooling home schooling	one word, may be hyphenated, or two words
Noun + Preposition	passer-by	hyphenated
Adjective + Noun	Sacred Scripture	two words
Adjective + Verb	Lenten fasting	two words
Verb + Noun	practicing Catholic	two words
Preposition + Noun	in-law	hyphenated

When the combination of words is used to identify a person, place, thing, or idea, then the words form a compound noun. Compound names may be placed together as in the word "godparents." They may remain separated as in "Sacred Scripture," or they may be hyphenated as in "sister-in-law." Homeschooling may be one word, two words, or hyphenated. You will need to use a dictionary to determine the correct form of compound nouns.

FORMING COMPOUND NOUNS EXERCISE

Use a dictionary to determine how to form these compound nouns. The dictionary may provide two options. Choose the first option provided.

Example: cup + cake *cupcake*

1. butter + cup _____

2. peanut + butter _____

3. super + nova _____

4. grace + note _____

5. alms + giving _____

6. sight + singing _____

7. forget + me + not _____

8. in + sight _____

9. good + will _____

10. morning + glory _____

11. mother + in + law _____

12. honey + comb _____

Forming More Compound Nouns Exercise

Use your dictionary to determine the correct way to form these compound nouns.

1. dining + room _____

2. bed + room _____

3. room + mate _____

4. room + temperature _____

5. gold + smith _____

6. golden + rule _____

7. grass + hopper _____

8. grass + snake _____

9. White + House _____

10. white + out _____

11. life + cycle _____

12. life + time _____

Compound Words

Beware! Not all word combinations will be compound nouns. Compound words may be adjectives or verbs.

Examples: "Overarching" is a verb, not a compound noun. "Well-read" is an adjective.

An adjective next to a noun may not form a compound noun.

Examples: "High school" is a compound noun, but "small school" is not. "Yellow butter" is not a compound noun, but "peanut butter" is.

How can you determine if a word or words form a compound noun? Use a dictionary. You will find "high school" and "peanut butter" in the dictionary, but you will not find "small school" or "yellow butter" there. However, you will find "small-town" and "yellow fever" in the dictionary. If you find the word in a dictionary, then you know the word is a compound noun although the dictionary does not list every compound noun.

COMPOUND NOUNS OR NOT EXERCISE

Using the context of the following sentences, write CN only if the underlined word or words form a compound noun. If you are not sure, use the dictionary.

Example: _____ The <u>small school</u> had only twenty students. (Do not write CN because "small school" is not a compound noun.)

1. _____ Sopranos, altos, tenors, and basses assembled in the <u>choir loft</u>.

2. _____ The <u>choirmaster</u> arrived, and the singers turned to face him.

3. _____ The music filling the air seemed almost <u>supernatural</u>.

4. _____ The <u>well-known</u> verses caught the attention of Sr. Margaret who was walking past.

5. _____ Sr. Margaret <u>tiptoed</u> quietly by the room so as not to disturb the rehearsal.

6. _____ <u>Gregorian chant</u> inspired and encouraged her.

7. _____ <u>Mother Superior</u> had asked to speak with her, so Sr. Margaret continued on her way out.

8. _____ With the music growing fainter, Sr. Margaret quickly descended the stairs and headed across the street toward the <u>walled convent</u>.

9. _____ Sr. Margaret found Mother Superior busy mending an <u>altar cloth</u>.

Hyphenated Compound Noun Exercise

Underline the three compound nouns in the following verse by James Whitcomb Riley, but don't get confused by all the hyphens. Not every hyphenated word is a compound noun. Ask yourself if the word identifies a person, place, thing, or idea.

I ain't a-goin' to cry no more, no more!

I'm got ear-ache, an' Ma can't make

It quit a-tall;

An' Carlo bite my rubber-ball

An' puncture it; an' Sis she take

An' poke' my knife down through the stable-floor

An' loozed it — blame it all!

But I ain't goin' to cry no more, no more!

More Compound Nouns Exercise

Fr. Gerard Manley Hopkins often created hyphenated compound words in his poetry. Enjoy the poem and find eight examples of compound nouns. Two of the compound nouns are not hyphenated. Be careful not to confuse compound adjectives with compound nouns.

The Starlight Night

Look at the stars! look, look up at the skies!

O look at all the fire-folk sitting in the air!

The bright boroughs, the circle-citadels there!

Down in dim woods, the diamond delves! the elves'-eyes!

The grey lawns cold where gold, where quickgold lies!

Wind-beat whitebeam! airy abeles set on a flare!

Flake-doves sent floating forth at a farmyard scare!—

Ah well! it is all a purchase, all is a prize.

Buy then! bid then!—What?—Prayer, patience, alms, vows.

Look, look: a May-mess, like on orchard boughs!

  Look! March-bloom, like on mealed-with-yellow sallows!

These are indeed the barn; withindoors house

The shocks. This piece-bright paling shuts the spouse

  Christ home, Christ and his mother and all his hallows.

  (A whitebeam and an abele are two types of trees that both have leaves with white undersides. A sallow is a willow tree that has large yellow fuzzy flowers appearing before the leaves appear.)

Review of Compound Sentences

Turn these simple sentences into compound sentences by using a comma and a conjunction, a semicolon, or a comma if the simple sentences are very short.

Example: Man proposes. God disposes. *Man proposes, God disposes.*

1. In springtime, we prepared the flower beds. And we planted seeds.

    _____

    _____

2. This year, we planted snapdragons, love-in-a-mist, and bee balm. But we didn't plant forget-me-nots.

    _____

    _____

3. We watered. We weeded.

    _____

4. The sunshine warmed the earth. The rain fell gently.

    _____

    _____

5. Our flowers grew and bloomed. And we gathered them to give to Grandmother on her birthday.

    _____

    _____

Can you find nine compound nouns in the above sentences?

_____ _____ _____

_____ _____ _____

_____ _____ _____

Possessive Nouns

Nouns that show ownership or belonging are possessive nouns. If the noun is singular, we add an 's to indicate possession. Remember that some singular nouns end in s.

Examples: Singular nouns—the computer's memory, the octopus's prey, Bess's coat

(You may omit the s for singular words ending in s, especially if the phrase sounds awkward, but be consistent.)

SINGULAR POSSESSIVE NOUNS EXERCISE

Change the following phrases to create singular possessive nouns.

Example: the coat owned by Father _____*Father's coat*_____

1. the math book belonging to Peter _____

2. the DVD that Lucy bought _____

3. the leash of the dog _____

4. the rosary we gave to Sr. Agnes _____

5. the generosity of the O'Callaghan family _____

Plural Names

Names ending in *ch*, *s*, *sh*, and *z* can be confusing unless you consider whether you are referring to one person or more than one person. Mr. Davis (one person) and all the little Davises (more than one person) went for ice cream. They got into Mrs. Davis's (one person's) big car. They drove to the Suarez Ice Cream Shop downtown. The little Suarezes (more than one person) were great friends with the little Davises (more than one person), and Mr. Davis (one person) and Mr. Suarez (one person) knew each other well. Then Mrs. O'Grady (one person) pulled into the parking lot. All the O'Gradys (more than one person) rushed into the ice cream shop.

PLURAL NAMES EXERCISE

Change each singular name to make it plural.

Examples: Burch—The Burches live next door to us.

1. Carlos—The three _____ I know are great friends with each other.

2. Jones—The _____ live in a twelve-bedroom house.

3. MacIntosh—I met the five _____ in the library.

4. Valdez—We visited with the _____ over the weekend.

5. Larch—The _____ are both police officers.

Plural Possessive Nouns

If a plural noun already ends in an s, we add only the apostrophe '.

Examples of Plural Nouns: the citizens' votes, the Davises' chickens, the Suarezes' backyard, but the men's boots

PLURAL POSSESSIVE NOUNS EXERCISE

Change the following phrases to create plural possessive nouns.

Example: the dogs belonging to the Valdezes   *The Valdezes' dogs*

1. the Masses celebrated for the children _____

2. the voices of the singers _____

3. the stalls for the horses _____

4. the cars belonging to the Joneses _____

5. the tears that the babies are crying _____

6. the badges that the Larches wear _____

The following names are almost always written without the final s:

   Jesus' Holy Face, or more commonly, The Holy Face of Jesus

   Moses' Laws, or more commonly, The Laws of Moses

   Socrates' philosophy

   Descartes' logic

   Achilles' heel

Singular and Plural Possessive Nouns Exercise

Underline the possessive nouns in the following essay:

Stephen Hawking's book *A Brief History of Time* is a best-selling science book, which was published on April Fools' Day, 1988. It's not easy to understand how such a book could become a bestseller. In chapter one, Hawking describes Nicolaus Copernicus's model of the universe, Isaac Newton's laws, and Edwin Hubble's observations. The Hubble Telescope, which has recorded beautiful images of the universe from its orbit around the Earth, is named after Edwin Hubble. Although the book explains complicated mathematical concepts, it contains only one equation, Einstein's $E=mc^2$. The information in later chapters is mind-boggling. What will be the physical universe's fate? Will the uncertainty principle lead some scientists to be more open-minded about God's dominion in the universe? Hawking mentions the Catholic Church's views and actions in several places in this book. Science and faith aren't always comfortable in each other's company, but as stated in Pope John Paul II's encyclical "Faith and reason are like two wings on which the human spirit rises to the contemplation of truth; and God has placed in the human heart a desire to know the truth."

Writing Possessive Nouns Exercise

Write a list of six objects in your household—three objects that belong to your family and three objects that belong to different people or animals in your family. If your last name ends in the letters s, ch, sh, or z, then make the name plural by adding es, as "the Stevenses' trampoline" and "the Rodriguezes' barn."

Example: Mike's trombone, the girls' bedroom

1. _____

2. _____

3. _____

4. _____

5. _____

6. _____

Collective Nouns

Collective nouns are the specific names we give to collections or groups of things. Although the collective noun refers to members of a group, the noun is singular and takes a singular verb when the members are acting as one unit.

Example: A <u>pod</u> of whales is feeding.

All the whales of the group, which is called a pod, are feeding.

Sometimes the members of the group are mentioned, as in the pod <u>of whales</u>, and sometimes the members are not specifically mentioned as in the following example.

Example: The <u>army</u> is practicing maneuvers.

The members of the army are understood to be soldiers, and each soldier is acting with the others as part of one army.

We also use plural collective nouns, especially in sports.

Example: The two <u>teams</u> compete against each other on the playing field.

Two distinct groups are playing against each other.

COLLECTIVE NOUNS EXERCISE

Underline the collective nouns in the following sentences.

Example: We decided to join the <u>crowd</u>, which had gathered in the street to support the sanctity of life.

1. The company is growing quickly and added thirty new employees last month.

2. The professor gave the same test to his four classes of math students.

3. My family likes to eat outside under the shade of the oak trees.

4. In a few minutes, the jury will announce its decision.

5. The juggler joined a troupe of musicians and traveled around the country.

6. The ship's crew was tired from swabbing the decks.

7. God created hosts of angels.

8. Plagues of locusts destroy crops from time to time.

Matching Collective Nouns and Members Exercise

Use a dictionary to match the collective nouns in the Word Bank to these specific groups of animals and people.

_____ of peacocks

_____ of larks

_____ of lambs

_____ of grasshoppers

_____ of vicars

_____ of knights

_____ of mourners

_____ of bishops

Word Bank

bench	fall
muster	exaltation
cortege	cloud
banner	prudence

Creating Collective Nouns Exercise

Invent your own collective nouns. Mix and match the collective nouns in Column A with the groups in Column B. Several choices are possible.

A	B
an accompaniment	of holy days
a cacophony	of altar servers
a beautification	of uneducated minds
a blessing	of virtues
a calendar	of religious sisters
a confusion	of owls
a wisdom	of thunderstorms

Appositives

An appositive is a word or word phrase that identifies or explains a noun. Appositives usually follow the noun, but they may also immediately precede it. Appositives that are required to understand the meaning of the sentence should not be set off with commas as in the last example.

Examples:

Mary, <u>the Mother of God</u>, went to visit Elizabeth.

We enjoyed visiting many significant ruins in Rome, <u>an ancient city</u>.

<u>The apostle to the Gentiles and the former persecutor of Christians</u>, Paul suffered greatly during his travels.

James <u>the son of Zebedee</u> died as a martyr before James <u>the son of Alphaeus</u> died.

APPOSITIVES EXERCISE

Underline the appositives in the sentences below and write the noun the appositive is referring to.

Example: Mr. Golightly, <u>the tour guide</u>, greeted the travelers.

Mr. Golightly

1. Kolbe and Marie went with their parents on a trip to Rome, The Eternal City.

_____

2. On the first day of their trip, Kolbe took a photograph of the Arch of Constantine, a monument built around 315 A.D. to honor the triumph of Constantine at the Battle of Milvian Bridge.

_____

3. Marie, the artist of the family, sat down to sketch in St. Peter's Basilica on the second day.

_____

4. Mr. and Mrs. Laurent, the children's parents, were astounded at the beauty of the statues, especially the Pietà.

_____

5. Michelangelo's famous marble sculpture shows Mary holding the body of Christ her son after His death.

_____

6. One of the holiest Christian sites and the burial place of St. Peter, the Basilica houses many artistic masterpieces.

_____

7. The Laurent family, parents and children, agreed that one week was not long enough to see everything they wanted to see.

_____

Appositive or Not Exercise

Write Appositive *if the sentence contains an appositive.*

Example: _____Appositive_____ The famous author C.S. Lewis knew many other well-known writers. (The appositive is "The famous author.")

1. _____ The movie trilogy *The Lord of the Rings* was based on J. R. R. Tolkien's literary masterpiece by the same name.

2. _____ The books and the movies feature the hobbits Frodo and Sam.

3. _____ Frodo, the heir of Bilbo, must take charge of a secret ring.

4. _____ This ring corrupts its wearers and may cause the end of Middle-Earth.

5. _____ The ring can only be destroyed by casting it into the fires of Mount Doom, a volcano in the midst of the stronghold of the enemy.

6. _____ Will Sam be of any assistance to Frodo on the journey to Mount Doom?

7. _____ Or will Sauron, the enemy of all that is good and beautiful in Middle-Earth, find and use the ring to enslave men, dwarves, elves, and hobbits?

Writing Appositives Exercise

Write your own appositives or nouns.

1. My pet _____ pays attention when I call his name.

2. We plan to visit New York City, _____ .

3. The Bishop of Rome, _____ , travels to many countries.

4. When she was young, Mother Teresa, _____ , decided she wanted to devote her

    life to God.

5. I always ask for _____ , my favorite kind of cake, on my birthday.

Review of Nouns

Identify the underlined word or word phrase as an appositive, a singular possessive noun, a plural possessive noun, or a collective noun.

1. The <u>marching band</u> was waiting patiently in line in the heat of midday to participate in the Fourth of July parade. _____

2. Mr. Abraham Langley, <u>the mayor</u>, was mopping his forehead.

   _____

3. The <u>horses' bridles</u> were gleaming in the sunlight. _____

4. <u>Mrs. Elizabeth Davis's dress</u> was spectacular with red, white, and blue ribbons.

   _____

5. <u>The patriotic theme</u> "Remember Our Heroes" was emblazoned on a large banner.

   _____

6. The <u>crowd</u> lining each side of the street was enormous and noisy.

   _____

7. The little <u>Joneses' squeals</u> of excitement suddenly rang out when they saw their grandfather marching and playing his tuba. _____

Verbs

Verbs do the work of the sentence. Linking verbs link a subject to a condition, helping verbs help other verbs, and action verbs show action. The helping verbs and the verb tense will indicate the time of the action or condition.

Let's look at verbs that link subjects and conditions. Common linking verbs are listed.

> am, is, are, was, were
> appear, seem, look, become
> sound, smell, taste, feel
> remain, get, prove

Example: I am cold.

No action is taking place. "Am" is linking "I" to "cold."

Example: The children were hungry.

What word is linking children to hungry? The verb "were" links the subject "children" to the condition of being hungry. No action is taking place.

Example: The books seemed ancient.

The verb "seemed" is linking which two words? The verb links "books" with "ancient." No action is taking place.

I smell pizza.

Is "smell" linking "I" to "pizza," or is an action taking place? Action is taking place. I am smelling the pizza.

Example: The pizza smells wonderful.

Is the pizza performing an action? No. Now the verb "smell" is linking "pizza" to "wonderful."

USING LINKING VERBS EXERCISE

Delete the incorrect linking verbs from the choices provided, leaving the correct linking verb.

Example: The flowers (~~am become~~ are) red with white centers.

"Oh, Fido! You (is smell appears) terrible."

"I thought dogs had a highly trained sense of smell."

"They do. But that (is was am) not what I mean. I mean that Fido needs a bath so that his fur will smell and (felt feel feeling) nice."

"I understand. He (was seemed appeared) naughty and rolled in that dead skunk out in the back this morning. I guess his highly trained sense of smell (proved seemed remained) a real nuisance in this case. "

"Oh, dear! That explains why he (looks smells am) quite pleased with himself."

"Fido hates baths. He will not (have remain become) happy for long."

Linking a Subject and a Noun

In the first linking verb exercise, most of the linking verbs linked the subject to an adjective. Fido smelled terrible. Fido is linked to the adjective terrible. But linking verbs can also connect the noun of the subject to a noun in the predicate.

Noun   Noun

Example: My mother is a doctor.

The linking verb "is" gives more information about my mother.

Example: The first bridge they crossed was a wooden log over a stream.

The complete subject is "The first bridge they crossed." This subject is linked by "was" to "a wooden log over a stream."

COMPLETING THE LINKING VERB EXERCISE

Write a noun or noun phrase to complete the sentence.

Examples: Hydrogen is ___*the simplest element*___ .

My brother may become ___*a Nobel Prize winner*___ some day.

1. Science is the _____ .

2. Albert Einstein was a _____ .

3. Is Stephen Hawking also a _____ ?

4. Madame Curie was a _____ .

5. I am not a _____ .

6. Some day, I will be a _____ .

Linking Verb or Not Exercise

Write LV if the verb or verb phrase is used as a linking verb. Write AV if the verb is an action verb.

Examples:

__AV__ I tasted the hamburgers while grilling them.

__LV__ The hamburgers tasted deliciously smoky.

1. _____ Harvey Mancini is a nurse.

2. _____ Harvey Mancini is busy.

3. _____ The oak tree in the front yard grew taller and taller.

4. _____ The oak tree in the front yard grew acorns.

5. _____ The cat appears drowsy.

6. _____ The cat appears on the front door step in the afternoon.

7. _____ Marissa Fabourg remained hungry after eating a salad.

8. _____ Marissa Fabourg remained in the café after eating.

9. _____ The electronic gadget looks expensive.

10._____ She looks at the expensive electronics.

PARTS OF SPEECH

Photocopying of these pages is a violation of copyright law.

37

Another Linking Verb Exercise

Some of the verbs are linking verbs and some are not. Underline only the linking verbs.

Examples: The apostles <u>were</u> fishermen. (The linking verb *were* links apostles to fishermen.)

The apostles were preaching in the synagogues. (In this example, *were* acts with preaching to indicate the tense or time of the action. *Were* is acting as a helping verb not a linking verb.)

1. The Pope is elected as the Successor of Peter.

2. Jesus chose Peter as the first Pope.

3. The popes appear frail to some, but they have the strength of the truth.

4. We become confused when we look only at the surface of things.

5. The truth seems old-fashioned to some people.

6. It sounds false to those who follow trends.

7. Yet the Church and the truth remain strong and reliable for Catholics around the world.

Action Verbs

Action verbs put a sentence in motion. An action may be a slow motion, such as sleeping, or a lively motion, such as dancing. We can not have a sentence without a verb.

WRITING VERBS EXERCISE

Write verbs to complete these sentences.

Example: _____Jump_____ through all the

hoops.

1. The dancers swing and _____ .

2. The citizens _____ the tea in

   the harbor to protest taxes.

3. The volcano _____ and

   frightened the townspeople.

4. You may _____ the

   chocolate cake.

5. Don't _____ the lemonade.

6. _____ the chores, and then

   we'll go to the movies.

7. The parishioners _____ to

   pray the Rosary.

LOCATING ACTION VERBS

Find four action verbs in these verses from Fr. John Bannister Tabb's poem "The Swallow." The italicized words are not verbs, but verb forms used as adjectives.

Skim o'er the tide,

And from thy pinions fling

The *sparkling* water-drops,

Sweet child of spring!

Bathe in the *dying* sunshine warm and bright,

Till ebbs the last *receding* wave of light.

Helping Verbs

Helping verbs assist other verbs. There are twenty-three helping verbs that may appear with main verbs to form verb phrases:

be	being	been	am	is	are	was	were
will	can	shall	may	might	must		
do	does	did	should	could	would		
have	had	has					

Why would other verbs need assistance?

Verbs need help **to indicate the time** of the action, or the time of the condition for linking verbs.

Example: The family <u>had</u> worked together all morning.

The helping verb "had" assists the verb "worked" to indicate that the family is no longer working together. The action is finished.

Verbs need help **to indicate ability, possibility, permission, necessity.**

Example: The family <u>must</u> work together all morning.

The helping verb "must" in the verb phrase "must work" tells us that the family should work together all morning. Perhaps they have a job that can only be done with everyone's aid.

Helping verbs can be combined to say exactly what you mean.

Example: The tri-athletes <u>have</u> already <u>been</u> swimming, but they <u>are</u> now bicycling, and soon they <u>will be</u> running.

Note that "already" and "now" are not verbs but adverbs. Adverbs may separate verbs in a verb phrase.
"Not" is commonly found mixed in with verb phrases, but it is not a verb.

LOCATING HELPING VERBS EXERCISE

Underline the helping verbs. Write the main verb in the blank. Remember that other words may be placed between verbs in a verb phrase.

1. Wesley and Anne are helping their parents with yard work. _____

2. They have been raking leaves all morning. _____

3. Wesley would rake together piles of leaves, and Anne would take the leaves to the compost pile.

   _____   _____

4. The compost pile was already spilling over. _____

5. Their parents have been trimming the shrubs. _____

6. The trimmings will not fit in the compost pile. _____

7. Should the family start a new compost pile? _____

Contracted Helping Verbs

Some helping verbs and linking verbs are attached as contractions to nouns and pronouns.

Example: We'll play tennis on Saturday.

> The helping verb is "will," but "will" has been contracted with the pronoun "We" to form "We'll."

Example: I've bought a red racing bicycle.

> "I've" stands for "I have," and "have" is the helping verb.

CONTRACTIONS AND HELPING VERBS EXERCISE

Write out the complete helping verb.

Examples: She's not going to the grocery store. _____*is*_____

He won't forget. _____*will*_____ ("won't" stands for "will not," and "not" is not a verb.)

1. We're discovering that juggling is difficult but amusing. _____

2. They'll retrieve any dropped juggling balls. _____

3. They don't know how to juggle yet. _____

4. We won't drop any balls if we're careful. _____

5. They've been watching us for ten minutes. _____

6. He shouldn't laugh at our mistakes. _____

7. I'm getting tired of juggling now. _____

Review of Verbs

Write HV over the helping verbs, V over action verbs, and LV over linking verbs in this verse from Joyce Kilmer's poem "Houses."

And when night <u>comes</u> down on Heaven-town

    (If there <u>should be</u> night up there)

You <u>will choose</u> the house you <u>like</u> the best

    Of all that you <u>can see</u>:

And its walls <u>will glow</u> as you drowsily <u>go</u>

    To the bed up the golden stair,

And I <u>hope</u> you<u>'ll be</u> gentle enough to keep

    A room in your house for me.

Verb Tenses

We mentioned that helping verbs help to show the time of the action or condition. A verb may also change its form to indicate time. The meaning of our sentences often depends upon time.

Did the action or condition take place in the past?
Is it taking place now?
Will it take place in the future?

We divide time into past, present, and future. Each of these basic divisions can be divided even further for more precise meaning. We can express complex time relationships based upon the verb form or helping verbs we choose.

PAST, PRESENT, OR FUTURE EXERCISE

Write "Past," "Present," or "Future" in the blank to indicate the time of the action or condition of the underlined verb or verb phrase.

Examples: I <u>am walking</u> my dog. *Present*

The dog <u>chewed</u> a bone. *Past*

The dog <u>will take</u> a nap in the afternoon.

  Future

1. Alfred Joyce Kilmer <u>was born</u> in December, 1886 in New Jersey.

   _____

2. The house where he was born <u>is</u> still <u>standing</u>.

   _____

3. In June 1908, Kilmer <u>married</u> Aline Murray.

   _____

4. They <u>had</u> five children. _____

5. Their youngest child <u>contracted</u> polio, which causes paralysis, and died young.

   _____

6. Her suffering and much prayer <u>led</u> Joyce and Aline Kilmer to a decision to convert to Catholicism.

   _____

7. Kilmer <u>died</u> at the age of 31 while fighting in World War I in France.

   _____

8. He <u>was scouting</u> for the position of a German machine gun when a sniper shot him.

   _____

9. If you visit Elmwood Cemetery in New Brunswick, New Jersey, you <u>will see</u> a monument to the fallen hero.

   _____

10. You <u>can read</u> the well-known poem "Trees" by Joyce Kilmer.

   _____

Writing Verb Tenses Exercise

Write the correct verb tense in the blank to change the timing of the sentence.

Examples: Present – The priest _____*prays*_____ the Rosary.

Past – The priest _____*prayed*_____ the Rosary.

Future – The priest _____*will pray*_____ the Rosary.

1. Future – The explorers _____ the steep mountain. (climb)

2. Present – The explorers _____ the steep mountain. (climb)

3. Past – The explorers _____ the steep mountain. (climb)

4. Present – Mother _____ chocolate chip cookies. (serve)

5. Past – Mother _____ chocolate chip cookies. (bake)

6. Future – Mother _____ chocolate chip cookies. (eat)

7. Past – The Cherokee hunters _____ a deer. (kill)

8. Present – The Cherokee hunters _____ a deer. (track)

9. Future – The Cherokee hunters _____ a deer to feed their hungry families. (kill)

Progressive Verbs

Progressive verbs express an action or condition that is ongoing. Many of our actions and conditions are not instantaneous. They take time and patience. Progressive verbs allow us to express continuous action or conditions.

Examples: Present Progressive — My children <u>are growing</u>. (They do not grow up instantly because growth takes time.)

Past Progressive — They <u>were studying</u> for a math exam. (While we might like to study quickly, studying for an exam takes patience.)

Future Progressive — The dog <u>will be getting</u> a bath tomorrow. (Baths probably seem to last an eternity to the dog if he doesn't enjoy them.)

Notice that progressive verbs end in –ing and require helping verbs to make the meaning clear.

USING PRESENT PROGRESSIVE VERBS EXERCISE

Choose the correct present progressive verb form to complete each sentence.

Example: They _____*are talking*_____ to the musicians. (are talking, is talking, am talking)

1. Mary and Joseph _____ to Bethlehem. (am traveling, is traveling, are traveling)

2. They _____ for an inn. (are looking, is looking, am looking)

3. Mary _____ weary from the journey. (am growing, is growing, are growing)

4. Joseph _____ worried about his wife. (is becoming, am becoming, are becoming)

5. I _____ if you know the ending to this story. (is wondering, are wondering, am wondering)

Finding Past Progressive Verbs Exercise

Underline the past progressive verbs in the sentences below. Not every sentence will have a past progressive verb, and some sentences will have more than one.

Example: When you <u>were studying</u>, I <u>was cleaning</u> my room.

1. William Shakespeare lived during politically dangerous times.

2. Queen Elizabeth <u>was ruling</u> England at that time.

3. Government authorities <u>were persecuting</u> Catholics for their faith.

4. While the Queen <u>was demanding</u> adherence to the Church of England, many Catholics <u>were holding</u> fast to their faith.

5. The English court <u>was summoning</u> many suspected Catholics, including Shakespeare's father.

6. When Shakespeare's father refused to appear in court, he was fined a large sum.

7. During the time Shakespeare <u>was writing</u> his plays in London, he <u>was renting</u> rooms.

8. As a householder, he would have been expected to sign church records that he had received communion.

9. Historians looked for his signature on many church records and found nothing.

10. Perhaps because Shakespeare <u>was growing</u> more popular, government authorities chose not to persecute him.

Writing Future Progressive Verbs Exercise

Complete the sentences with the correct helping verbs and verb forms to indicate an on-going action in the future.

Example: We ___*will be traveling*___ to France next year. (travel)

1. Mother _____ us how to speak a few words in French. (teach)

2. Father _____ French churches we can visit. (research)

3. My brothers _____ famous French musicians every night. (discuss)

4. My sisters _____ French cheeses during the trip. (taste)

5. I _____ all the sights of France every day of the trip. (photograph)

6. We _____ carefully for a wonderful trip. (preparing)

Past, Present, or Future Progressive Exercise

Underline the progressive verb phrase and write "Past," "Present," or "Future."

Example: ___Past___ The rhinoceros <u>was charging</u> at the unfortunate photojournalists.

1. _____ The snake will be warming itself in the sun.

2. _____ The deer are sleeping in the shadows of the forest.

3. _____ The opossum will be waking up as the sun sets.

4. _____ The armadillo was snuffling for insects in the rotten log.

5. _____ Because it was noon, the sun's rays were fiercely striking the tops of our heads.

6. _____ I am walking as quietly as I can.

7. _____ The cardinal was singing on the top of the tree stump.

8. _____ This hike is challenging our endurance because it is ten miles long.

9. _____ What animal is watching us from the safety of the thick brush?

Irregular Verbs

Many verbs are regular and follow a pattern for changing tenses. The simple verb form is used for present tense. Past tense requires an -ed ending as in the following example. The past perfect tense, which you have not yet studied, means that an action has been completed in the past.

Regular Verb:
Present—Mother <u>bakes</u>.   (the -s is added for third person singular)
Past—Mother <u>baked</u>. (also used as an adjective—the <u>baked</u> bread)
Past Perfect—Mother <u>had baked</u>.
Future—Mother <u>will bake</u>.

Not all verbs follow the same regular pattern for changing tenses. The verbs that stray from the pattern are called irregular verbs.

Irregular Verb:
Present — Placido Domingo <u>sings</u> well. (the -s is added for third person singular)
Past — Placido Domingo <u>sang</u> well yesterday.
Past Perfect — Placido Domingo <u>had sung</u> in many countries. (also used as an adjective—the <u>sung</u> Mass)
Future—Placido Domingo <u>will sing</u> tonight.

The simple verb form "be" is common and highly irregular. A simple verb form is the verb without any endings. It is not a verb tense, but it may be used to form verb tenses, such as the present tense.

The present tense forms are **am, is**, and **are**.
The past tense is **was** and **were**.
The past perfect tense is **been**.
The progressive tense is **being**.

CHANTING COMMON IRREGULAR VERBS EXERCISE

Chant these common irregular verbs aloud. The past perfect tense requires a helping verb to be complete, but we will not add the helping verbs in this exercise. Some verbs have more than one form that is correct, such as awoke/awaked.

Simple Verb	Past Tense	Past Perfect Tense
awake	awoke/awaked	awaked/awoken
become	became	become
begin	began	begun
bite	bit	bitten/bit
blow	blew	blown
break	broke	broken
bring	brought	brought
choose	chose	chosen
come	came	come
cut	cut	cut
dive	dived/dove	dived
do	did	done
draw	drew	drawn
drink	drank	drunk
eat	ate	eaten
fall	fell	fallen
fly	flew	flown
forgive	forgave	forgiven
go	went	gone
grow	grew	grown
have	had	had
know	knew	known
lay	laid	laid
lie	lay	lain
read	read	read
rise	rose	risen
speak	spoke	spoken
take	took	taken
tear	tore	torn
write	wrote	written

PARTS OF SPEECH

Completing the Verb Forms Exercise

Fill in the missing irregular verb forms, using the simple verb form, the past tense, and the past perfect tense in that order. The past perfect tense needs a helping verb (has, had, or having been) to be complete, but we will ignore the helping verb for this exercise. Use a dictionary if necessary.

Examples:

ride ___*rode*___ ridden

___*strive*___ strove striven

1. ring rang _____

2. think _____ thought

3. _____ wore worn

4. quit quit _____

5. say _____ said

6. _____ spent spent

7. throw threw _____

8. be was/were _____

9. do _____ done

10. _____ broke broken

Irregular and Regular Verbs Exercise

If the underlined verb is regular, write "R" in the blank. If the underlined verb is irregular, write "I." Write the simple tense for regular verbs and the three irregular forms for irregular verbs. Use a dictionary if necessary.

Examples:

_R_   We <u>looked</u> for the buried treasure. _____look_____

_I_   We <u>sought</u> the buried treasure. _seek, sought, sought_

1. _____ The elves <u>enjoyed</u> lovely songs. _____

2. _____ The dwarves <u>did</u> not often sing with the elves. _____

3. _____ The elven songs have <u>enchanted</u> their listeners. _____

4. _____ Ancient people <u>knew</u> many songs and lamentations. _____

5. _____ Have you <u>written</u> any songs? _____

6. _____ In ancient Greece, the muses <u>were</u> spirits that inspired the creation of art, poetry, music, and dance. _____

7. _____ Psalm 95 has <u>called</u> people to greet God with a song of praise since the time of King David. _____

8. _____ Shakespeare <u>told</u> his audiences that "the earth has music for those who listen."

   _____

9. _____ We <u>chant</u> many beautiful verses during Mass that make us think of God and heaven.

   _____

Review of Verb Tenses

Give the correct form or tense of these verbs.

Examples: The past perfect of *choose* is _____*chosen*_____ .

The simple verb form of *is calling* is _____*call*_____ .

The future progressive of *hide* is _____*will be hiding*_____ .

Using "he" as the subject, the past tense of *be* is _____*was*_____ .

1. Using "I" as the subject, the present progressive of *catch* is _____ .

2. Using "she" as the subject, the present tense of *sing* is _____ .

3. Using "it" as a subject, the past perfect tense of *trample* is had _____ .

4. Using "they" as the subject, the past progressive tense of *speak* is _____ .

5. The future tense of *tell* is _____ .

6. Using "we" as the subject, the past perfect of *keep* is have _____ .

7. The future progressive tense of *remember* is _____ .

8. The simple verb form of *thought* is _____ .

9. The past tense of *swim* is _____ .

10. The simple verb form and the past tense, and the past perfect tense (with the helping verb

    "have") of *cut* is _____ .

Transitive Verbs

Transitive verbs are action verbs that have a direct object. Transitive comes from a Latin word which means "a going across," so the action is going across from the subject to an object. The direct object is the noun that is receiving the action of the verb.

Example: The girls climbed the ladder into the treehouse.

What is the subject? The subject is *the girls*.
What are the girls doing? The girls are *climbing*.
What is being climbed? The *ladder* is being climbed.
So the ladder is the direct object, and "climbed" is a transitive verb.

FINDING TRANSITIVE VERBS EXERCISE

Underline the transitive verbs in the sentences that go with the italicized objects.

Example: Rat <u>swam</u> *the River*.

1. Tired of spring cleaning, Mole wandered about the countryside until he encountered *Rat*.

2. They both boarded *a little rowboat* and took off downriver, looking for adventure.

3. Rat had thoughtfully packed *a picnic basket* full of sandwiches and drinks.

4. The prow of the boat touched *the edge* of an island.

5. They ate *a delicious lunch* and talked of this and that.

6. Mole met *Otter* who was a good friend of Rat's.

7. Mole knew *his manners* well and did not ask about Otter's sudden disappearance.

PARTS OF SPEECH

Photocopying of these pages is a violation of copyright law.

55

Writing Transitive Verbs Exercise

Write the correct tense of the transitive verbs and underline the direct object.

Example: Bella _____*drove*_____ the <u>van</u> to the library. (drive—past tense)

1. The gardener _____ tomato seedlings this spring. (plant—future tense)

2. The zookeeper _____ the elephants as the visitors watch. (bathe—present tense)

3. Many people _____ the marathon, featuring the top two runners in the world. (watch—present progressive)

4. Wanting to help, we _____ soup for the hungry volunteers. (heat—past tense)

5. Because of their interest in explorers, the family _____ the historic route taken by Lewis and Clark. (trace—past progressive)

6. Sr. Mary Elizabeth _____ the children's essays about their field trip to the miniature horse farm. (grade—present tense)

7. I _____ the English Channel, but I'm not yet strong enough. (swim—future tense)

PARTS OF SPEECH

56

Photocopying of copyrighted material is strictly illegal.

Intransitive Verbs

Intransitive verbs are action verbs that do not have a direct object. No action is carried across. *Arrive, complain, grow, die, lie, sleep, go* are examples of intransitive verbs.

Examples: The women arrived by train.

The subject is *women*, and the verb is *arrived*. What was being arrived? Nothing. By train tells us how the women arrived. Do not confuse the noun in prepositional phrases with a direct object. Ask yourself, "What is being _____ ?"

Misty sleeps soundly.

Soundly is an adverb telling how Misty sleeps. Therefore, it can not be a direct object.

The old oak tree died.

This simple sentence contains no noun other than the subject, the old oak tree.

We sat down to supper.

What is being sat on? We did not sit down on supper. Supper is not receiving the action of sit.

CHOOSING INTRANSITIVE VERBS EXERCISE

Delete the phrases containing transitive verbs to leave the intransitive verb phrases.

Example: The writers (talked and argued, ~~wrote letters, read books~~) for hours.

1. The older children were (kicking the football, bouncing the basketball, swinging up high).

2. The younger children are (watching a video, playing in the sand, making puppets).

3. Of course, the babies are (kicking their feet, sleeping, blinking their eyes).

4. Meanwhile, the dog (barks loudly, chews a bone, licks its fur).

5. Mother is (watching the baby, baking cookies, standing near the sandbox).

6. Father was (walking toward the swings, throwing a stick for the dog, holding the baby).

7. Grandmother and Grandfather (discuss politics, play cards, sit and swing with the older children).

8. Great Aunt Martha (is napping, combing her hair, making a sandwich).

Transitive or Intransitive Exercise

Write "T" if the underlined verb is transitive and "I" if the verb is intransitive. The sentences have been taken from hymns; some have been modified slightly.

Example: __T__ Oh God, You <u>create</u> a clean heart for me. (A clean heart is being created.)

__I__ We <u>celebrate</u> with songs of praise. (What is being celebrated? The songs of praise are how we are celebrating. We are celebrating God's love, which is not mentioned.)

1. _____ Christ Himself <u>has fasted</u>.

2. _____ Angels, <u>bring</u> your praises.

3. _____ Alone and fasting, Moses <u>saw</u> the loving God who gave the law.

4. _____ We <u>walk</u> the road, Lord Jesus, that You have trod.

5. _____ Jesus <u>shines</u> purer than all the angels heaven can boast.

6. _____ Sweet Sacrament, we <u>adore</u> Thee.

7. _____ How <u>can</u> I <u>love</u> You as I ought?

8. _____ The fairest Lord Jesus <u>rules</u> all nature.

9. _____ We <u>arise</u> in You, Christ, since we have died in You.

10. _____ Sweetest Lady, <u>bless</u> the land of our birth.

Review of Verbs

Underline the verb or verb phrase and write "LV" to indicate linking verbs, "HV" for helping verbs, "T" for transitive, and "I" for intransitive verbs.

Examples: The musicians <u>had played</u> for hours.

HV   I

Mrs. Vivian Vance <u>is</u> a doctor.

LV

1. The birch trees are dying because of a lack of water.

2. Mr. Thomas O'Malley sneezed suddenly.

3. Portia's stomach is rumbling.

4. We will paint the fence a bright blue.

5. The girls and boys are singing Christmas carols.

6. They ate supper very late.

7. The athletes are strong and confident.

Pronouns

Pronouns take the place of nouns or other pronouns.

<u>Who</u> is knocking? <u>She</u> is knocking.

The personal pronoun "she" takes the place of the interrogative pronoun "who." But <u>who</u> is <u>she</u>? <u>She</u> is Mrs. O'Malley. So who is knocking? Mrs. O'Malley is knocking.

We are going to study personal, possessive, indefinite, reflexive, intensive, and interrogative pronouns. Before we do that, let's pay attention to pronoun antecedents.

The antecedent is the noun which the pronoun is referring to. If the reader or listener doesn't understand who or what the pronoun antecedent is, confusion will result.

Examples:

Who's there?
Me.
Me, who?

Everyone can be referred to with the pronoun "me."

The judges said that the red team members were not yet ready.

This is clear, but if we replace the nouns with pronouns, we get "<u>They</u> said that <u>they</u> were not yet ready." Here we are trying to use one pronoun to replace two different pronoun antecedents and the meaning has changed.

FINDING ANTECEDENTS EXERCISE

The pronouns are written in italics. Underline the pronoun antecedent, the noun that the pronoun is referring to.

Example: <u>Marie</u> laughed when Mr. Jenkins told *her* a joke.

1. Mark's mother gave *him* a shopping list.

2. The books on the table are *yours*, Kim and Phyllis.

3. The rain came down everyday, and *it* flooded the streets.

4. How are *you* feeling today, Dr. Jones?

5. The cat washed *itself* clean after sleeping on dust bunnies.

6. *Whose* paper will you grade first, Kate's or Zachary's?

7. The president *himself* toured the disaster scene.

Personal Pronouns

Personal pronouns refer to specific persons or things. These pronouns must agree in number, gender, person, and case. Case refers to how a word is being used in a sentence. Is the word being used as a subject, an object, or a possessive?

Subjective Case: <u>I</u> am writing a letter.
Objective Case: Suzy is handing <u>me</u> a letter. The letter is for <u>me</u>.
Possessive case: That letter is <u>mine</u>.

The possessive case can also be used as the subject of a sentence. <u>Mine</u> is the one with the large stamp.

Do not confuse the possessive pronouns with possessive adjectives: <u>my</u> letter, <u>our</u> letter, <u>your</u> letter, <u>his</u> letter, <u>her</u> letter, <u>their</u> letter.

To use the possessive pronoun, you would say or write: That letter is <u>theirs</u>, <u>hers</u>, <u>his</u>, <u>yours</u>, <u>ours</u>, <u>mine</u>.

Subjective, Objective, Possessive		
	Singular	Plural
1st person—both genders	I, me, mine	we, us, ours
2nd person—both genders	you, you, yours	you, you, yours
3rd person—both genders		they, them, theirs
Masculine	he, him, his	
Feminine	she, her, hers	
Neuter (no gender)	it, it, its	

CHOOSING SUBJECTIVE SINGULAR AND PLURAL PRONOUNS EXERCISE

*Choose a pronoun to act as the **subject** of each sentence.*

Example: ____You____ are very late. (plural, 2nd person)

1. _____ had lost their way in the snow. (plural, 3rd person)

2. _____ rescued the snow-covered friends. (singular, feminine, 3rd person)

3. Her son found warm blankets, and _____ wrapped the blankets around the shivering

   guests. (singular, masculine, 3rd person)

4. _____ soon grew warm enough to talk. (plural, 3rd person)

5. _____ don't know why they were lost. (singular, 1st person)

6. _____ should keep reading the story to find out what happens. (plural, 1st person)

7. _____ is not a long story. (singular, neuter, 3rd person)

Choosing Objective Singular and Plural Pronouns Exercise

*Choose a pronoun to act as the **object** of the verb or preposition.*

Example: Mrs. Malinski gave ____*me*____ a cup of sugar. (singular, 1st person)

1. I thanked _____ and carried the sugar home. (singular, feminine, 3rd person)

2. Upon reaching home, I set _____ on the counter in the kitchen. (singular, neuter, 3rd person)

3. The two-year-old twins must have thought I had set the sugar there for _____ to investigate. (plural, 3rd person)

4. Well, I will allow _____ to guess what happened. (singular, 2nd person)

5. The sugar was spilled, and the twins came running to _____ in tears. (singular, 1st person)

6. Then I remembered how Mother had told _____ all that curiosity killed the cat, but in this case, curiosity spilled the sugar. (plural, 1st person)

Choosing Possessive Singular and Plural Pronouns Exercise

Choose the correct possessive pronoun to complete each sentence.

Example: ___*Ours*___ is the one with the long hair and floppy ears. (plural, 1st person)

1. The judge asked, "Which is _____ ?" (singular, 2nd person)

2. "_____ is over there," I answered. (singular, 1st person)

3. _____ was a commanding presence, so I knew she must be the judge or one of the judges. (singular, feminine, 3rd person)

4. I had said "mine," but the well-behaved greyhound was actually _____ because Pharaoh belonged to the whole family. (plural, 3rd person)

5. First place could be _____ if he continued to stand calmly and obey all commands. (singular, 3rd person)

6. My friends Amy and Carl walked up with their two beagles. "_____ are looking sharp today," I said. (plural, 2nd person)

7. "Look," said Amy. "_____ have nice red ribbons." (plural, 3rd person)

8. The owners of a beribboned poodle walked by. "_____ is well-decorated," Carl whispered. "But pink isn't one of the prize colors." (plural, 3rd person)

Indefinite Pronouns

Personal pronouns refer to specific people, while indefinite pronouns refer to unspecified nouns.

Common Indefinite Pronouns

anybody, anyone, anything	few
all	much, many
both	nobody, no one, nothing
each	none
everybody, everyone, everything	several
	somebody, someone, something

FINDING INDEFINITE PRONOUNS EXERCISE

Underline the indefinite pronouns. Some sentences have more than one indefinite pronoun.

Example: The Davis family sent invitations to <u>everyone</u>.

1. No one knew the correct answer, but several guessed.

2. Something went bump in the night, and everyone jumped.

3. None of us have exotic monkeys as pets.

4. Many were invited, but few responded.

5. Anything could have happened when the rhinoceros got off its leash.

6. Both of the twins wanted all of the cookies.

7. Each of the athletic teams contributed to the food drive for the St. Vincent de Paul Society.

8. We decided that something should be done immediately about the water leak.

Reflexive and Intensive Pronouns

Reflexive and intensive pronouns use the same forms, but have different functions.

Reflexive pronouns refer back to the subject. They indicate that the object of a sentence is the same as the subject and require a transitive verb.

The student also sent <u>himself</u> a copy of the essay.

The student is the subject of the sentence, and he is also an object receiving the copy.

Intensive Pronouns emphasize the subject of the sentence. They usually appear immediately after the subject.

I <u>myself</u> made that mess. *Or* I made that mess <u>myself</u>.

The sentence emphasizes that I am taking the blame for the mess. I am not receiving the action, but I am taking the responsibility.

Notice particularly the plural form "selves" in the chart below.

	Singular	Plural
1st person	myself	ourselves
2nd person	yourself	yourselves
3rd person—both genders		themselves
Masculine	himself	
Feminine	herself	
Neuter	itself	

CHOOSING REFLEXIVE AND INTENSIVE PRONOUNS EXERCISE

Using the chart, choose the correct reflexive pronoun that best completes each sentence.

Example: The choir called ___*themselves*___ "The Parish Festival Chorus."

1. Can you do that by _____ , or do you need help? (singular)

2. I made the black-bottom raspberry cream cake _____ .

3. The dog unwillingly took _____ out of the kitchen during the preparation of the

   special dessert. (neuter)

4. We requested an audience with the Queen and King _____ .

5. The Queen of Epicuria _____ proclaimed my cake was delicious.

6. The King of Epicuria was quietly eating and helped _____ to yet another slice.

7. "We _____ would like to present you with the Order of the Spatula in honor of

   this cake," they said grandly after the last crumb was gone.

8. The king and queen added, "Although you _____ did not get the opportunity to

   taste the cake, we assure you all that it was the ultimate black-bottom raspberry cream cake."

   (plural)

Distinguishing between Reflexive and Intensive Pronouns Exercise

Underline all reflexive and intensive pronouns. Label the sentences "Reflexive" or "Intensive."

Examples: _Reflexive_____ The cat licked itself clean.

         _Intensive_____ The cat itself was all black although it wore a white collar.

1. _____ The King of Epicuria wrote himself notes.

2. _____ The Queen considered herself lucky to have a personal secretary.

3. _____ The citizens of Epicuria themselves were not allowed to vote for or against the king and queen.

4. _____ Yet the citizens thought themselves fortunate because the king and queen used their common sense to judge all matters, including food contests.

5. _____ We ourselves do not live in Epicuria.

6. _____ However, last summer we bought ourselves tickets for the annual pie throwing contest.

7. _____ You yourself should visit Epicuria some day, especially if you are fond of pies.

8. _____ The pie itself is highly regarded in Epicuria.

9. _____ So bring a friend and get yourselves front row seats.

Interrogative Pronouns

The word "interrogative" comes from a Latin word "rogāre," which means "to ask." The interrogative pronouns are those pronouns we use when asking questions.

These pronouns may not have antecedents because the antecedent is unknown, which is why the question is being asked.

There are five interrogative pronouns: what, which, who, whom, whose.

"Who" and "which" are used as subjects.
<u>Who</u> is coming to dinner? (antecedent unknown)
<u>Which</u> hat is yours? (We don't know which hat in particular.)

"Whose" is a possessive pronoun.
<u>Whose</u> dirty shoes are on the clean sofa? (We do not know the owner of the dirty shoes, and the owner may wish to remain unknown.)

"Whom" acts as an object of a sentence. Many people confuse "who" and "whom." If you can replace the interrogative pronoun with hi<u>m</u> or the<u>m</u>, let the last letter of these objective pronouns clue you in to use who<u>m</u>.

To <u>whom</u> would you like to speak?
Would you like to speak to <u>him</u>?

Incorrect: Who would you like to speak to?
If this sentence were correct, then we would be able to change it to "Would you like to speak to he?"

<u>Whom</u> are you looking for?
Are you looking for <u>them</u>?

Incorrect: Who are you looking for?
Are you looking for <u>they</u>? No, you are looking for <u>them</u>.

In casual conversation, you will often hear "who" used incorrectly. Out of charity, please refrain from correcting others. However, please use "who" and "whom" correctly in your writing.

CHOOSING INTERROGATIVE PRONOUNS EXERCISE

Complete the interrogative sentences by writing the correct interrogative pronoun.

Example: __*What*__ is the answer to question number ten?

1. _____ vegetable would you like for Easter dinner, asparagus or broccoli?

2. At _____ time will the Easter Vigil begin?

3. _____ did you invite to the vigil Mass? (Remember the test: Did you invite they or them to

   the vigil Mass?)

4. _____ is celebrating the Easter Sunday Mass?

5. _____ chocolate bunny is melting on the porch?

6. _____ is cooking the ham for dinner?

7. _____ do you suspect of taste testing the mashed potatoes?

8. _____ Easter hat is blowing down the street?

9. _____ car should we take to church?

Review of Pronouns

Choose the correct pronoun to complete each sentence.

1. Reflexive feminine—The homeschooler was quizzing _____ in preparation for a

    test.

2. Interrogative: _____ is a pronoun antecedent?

3. Interrogative: _____ is the correct objective case, who or whom?

4. Indefinite: _____ can learn to use pronouns correctly.

5. Reflexive: "Should I ask _____ more questions?" she wondered.

6. Personal: "Are _____ still studying?" her mother asked.

7. Possessive, 1st person: "The good or bad grade will be _____," she answered.

8. Indefinite: "But _____ has ever failed my pronoun tests," her mother said.

9. Intensive: "And I _____ do not wish to be the first," she responded.

10. Personal, 3rd person, feminine: "Maybe I should have given _____ more

    pronoun exercises," thought the mother.

11. Possessive, plural, 1st person: "Is this grammar book _____, or did we borrow it

    from the Joneses?" the homeschooler asked.

12. Possessive, plural, 3rd person: "I think it is _____," her mother said, "And I think

    you should get some rest."

Adjectives

"It was a <u>dark</u> and <u>stormy</u> night."

"Dark" and "stormy" are adjectives telling us what kind of night it was. Adjectives modify nouns or pronouns. Adjectives modify by describing, limiting, or specifying people, places, things, or ideas.

Whose rhinoceros? <u>My</u> rhinoceros
What color rhinoceros? <u>My white</u> rhinoceros
What size rhinoceros? <u>My small white</u> rhinoceros
How many rhinoceroses? <u>My only small white</u> rhinoceros

We could continue but that is quite enough said about the rhinoceros. Don't overdose your writing with strings of adjectives.

CHOOSING ADJECTIVES EXERCISE

You need to contact your friend who is at a party, and so you call the hostess and describe your friend using only adjectives. Draw a line from each adjective below to the phrase "My friend is."

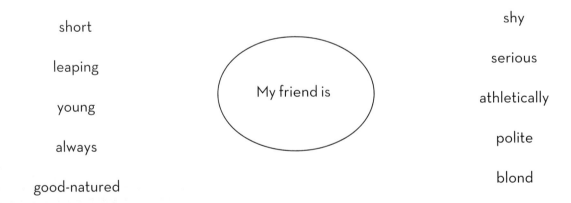

short

leaping

young

always

good-natured

My friend is

shy

serious

athletically

polite

blond

Finding Adjectives Exercise

In this version of Aesop's Fable "The Lion and the Bulls," underline the adjectives that modify the italicized nouns or pronouns.

Example: *She* is <u>lazy</u>.

Three *bulls* lived in a large, green *field*. The field was surrounded by dense *forest*, where a lion roamed. The *lion* was hungry yet cautious. *He* was strong, but *he* was also wise. He knew that he could not safely attack three *bulls*. So he called out to them, "Beware the fierce *lion* who attacks from the north." They moved to the south of the field. Then he called out, "Beware the angry *lion* who attacks from the south." The bulls began to argue about the safest *place* in the field. One went east and the other two *bulls* went west, and the lion attacked the lone *bull* and ate it.

Adverbs

Adverbs modify verbs, adjectives, or other adverbs. They tell when, where, and how something is happening. Many adverbs end in -ly, but some words ending in -ly are adjectives, such as lovely and friendly.

Adverbs Modifying Verbs:
When—We leave camp <u>today</u>.
The action of leaving is occurring today.

Where—Put the jewels <u>here</u>.
The adverb "here" tells us where the jewels will be placed.

How—The sinners begged <u>piteously</u> for mercy.
How did they beg? Proudly? No, they begged piteously.

Adverb Modifying an Adjective:
We were <u>too</u> quick to judge his character.
"Quick" is the adjective being modified by the adverb "too." This sentence has a negative meaning compared to the more factual "We were quick to judge his character."

Adverb Modifying an Adverb:
The adult wrote <u>more legibly</u> than the preschooler.
This sentence has two adverbs with "legibly" modifying the verb "wrote," and "more" modifying "legibly."

74

CHOOSING ADVERBS EXERCISE

Choose the adverb that best completes each sentence.

Example: The deer walked _____*cautiously*_____ along the trail. (shy, friendly, cautiously)

1. _____ many people filled the trails. (Yesterday, Lonely, Laughing)

2. _____ many people frighten the deer. (Too, Well, Completely)

3. If they walk _____ , they will not frighten away the deer. (madly, neighborly, quietly)

4. The early hikers _____ see many deer feeding. (tomorrow, often, absolutely)

5. When people go _____ in the evening, the fawns will appear. (home, fast, lovely)

6. _____ comes a fawn out of the underbrush. (Here, Lately, Sometimes)

ADVERB RELATIONSHIPS EXERCISE

Underline the word the italicized adverb is modifying.

Example: That train is moving *too* <u>fast</u>.

1. *Meticulously*, the train engineer looked over the day's schedule.

2. He was hauling a load of *very* dangerous chemicals.

3. His crew respected him *completely*.

4. They knew that he would act cautiously *today*.

5. He *calmly* gave instructions to the crew.

6. The train engineer *never* shouted unless there was an emergency.

7. They all climbed *aboard*.

Another Adverb Relationship Exercise

Find the adverbs and tell what part of speech the adverb is modifying. The words in parentheses explain the function of the adverb.

Example: Mack is waterskiing today. (when) The adverb _____today_____ is modifying the

___verb waterskiing___ .

1. Mack jumped onto the boat confidently. (how) The adverb _____ is

modifying the _____ .

2. He often shared his love of waterskiing. (when) The adverb _____ is

modifying the _____ .

3. Yesterday he skied with his fun-loving parents. (when) The adverb _____ is

modifying the _____ .

4. Then he took them home to rest. (where) The adverb _____ is modifying the

_____ .

5. They were quite tired from the exciting day of waterskiing. (how) The adverb

_____ is modifying the _____ .

6. Mack rarely missed a day of waterskiing. (when) The adverb _____ is

modifying the _____ .

7. In his family, he was the most skillful water skier. (how) The adverb _____ is

modifying the _____ .

Review of Adjectives and Adverbs

Determine whether the italicized words in the following sentences are adjectives or adverbs. Some sentences may contain both or more than one of each.

Example: The *red* embers popped *noisily*.

___Adjective___   ___Adverb___

1. The *rising* heat from the fire warmed the children's *cold* hands.

   _____ , _____

2. Father sat down beside them and *very quietly* began to tell them a ghost story.

   _____ , _____

3. Mr. James Bailey died of cholera, having left *strict* instructions as to his burial.

   _____

4. His wife's neighbors were *astounded* when they heard that James Bailey wished to be buried standing up with his rifle and a jug of whiskey.

   _____

5. Mrs. Bailey *finally* agreed to bury her husband in the *usual* manner—lying down and without a jug of whiskey.

   _____ , _____

6. After the burial, the neighbors began to see *wandering* lights out on the prairie where no light should be.

   _____

7. *Often* the children lifted their eyes from the fire to search Bailey's Prairie for signs of the *mysterious* lights.

   _____ , _____

8. Was the *unhappy* ghost of James Bailey *restlessly* wandering the prairie tonight?

   _____ , _____

(This is a short version of a ghost story that was often told to children in Brazoria County. James Bailey was an early settler of Texas, migrating from the eastern U.S. He died in 1832 when Texas still belonged to Mexico.)

PARTS OF SPEECH

Prepositions

Prepositions usually indicate position, time, and direction. They can also describe, tell how, why, by whom, to whom. Prepositions almost always combine with nouns to fulfill their function in a sentence. The noun is the object of the preposition.

Let's look at prepositions of position and direction. Imagine your church. You can use prepositions to tell where something is in relationship to your church—the parishioner is (in, near, far from, next to, within, outside, on, under) the church. If the parishioner is repairing the roof, then the parishioner would be located or positioned <u>on</u> the church. If the parishioner is headed <u>toward</u> the church, then you are using a preposition to indicate direction. "Church" would be the object of both the preposition "on" and the preposition "toward."

Prepositions can be combined together.
Example: They were standing <u>in front of</u> the church.

CHOOSING PREPOSITIONS OF POSITION AND DIRECTION EXERCISE

Complete these sentences by choosing a preposition.

Examples: The oak tree is growing ____*in*____ the forest. (position—the oak tree is not moving from one place to another)

The squirrel is running _*away from*_ the noise. (direction—the squirrel is in motion)

1. A squirrel is sitting _____ a branch of the oak tree. (position)

2. The squirrel is _____ the forest floor. (position)

3. Climbing _____ a branch, the squirrel gathers acorns at the ends of the branch. (direction)

4. After a while, the squirrel has gathered too many acorns, and one acorn falls _____ to the forest floor. (direction)

5. The acorn happens to land _____ the head of a person standing _____ the oak tree. (direction, position)

6. An eagle flies _____ the oak tree. (direction)

7. The cautious squirrel dives _____ a hollow in the trunk of the oak tree. (direction)

More Prepositions

Example: <u>With a dramatic flourish</u>, I presented a box <u>of chocolates</u> <u>to Kim</u> <u>for her birthday</u>.

    A sentence can be full of prepositions to express an exact meaning. In the example above, "With a dramatic flourish" tells how (the manner with which) I presented a box of chocolates. The preposition "of" describes what kind of box is being given. "Chocolate" is the object of the preposition.

    "To" is the next preposition and "Kim" is the object of the preposition because the sentence tells who received the box. The example uses yet another preposition to tell why Kim received the box—it was her birthday, and "birthday" is the object of the third preposition.

UNDERSTANDING PREPOSITIONS EXERCISE

Underline the prepositional phrase and tell why the preposition is used, using the list of functions provided.

Example: The shed is full <u>of tools</u>. _____ *description* _____

1. The children carried the heavy boxes without complaint. _____

2. The bookseller showed us the sonnets written by Shakespeare. _____

3. We gave a family photograph to our grandparents. _____

4. During the thunderstorm, the dogs slept soundly. _____

5. Put the spoons on the table. _____

6. We are driving across the country this summer. _____

7. People in colorful costumes are dancing and waving. _____

8. We prepared hamburgers for the party. _____

9. A feeling of excitement arose when the clown entered the room. _____

Functions of a Preposition

authorship	direction	manner	reason
description	giving/receiving	position	time

PARTS OF SPEECH

Finding Prepositions Exercise

Underline the prepositional phrases in these quotations by G.K. Chesterton.

Example: A dead thing can go <u>with the stream</u>, but only a living thing can go <u>against it</u>.

1. He is a [sane] man who can have tragedy in his heart and comedy in his head.

2. Tradition means giving votes to the most obscure of all classes, our ancestors.

3. The modern world is a crowd of very rapid racing cars all brought to a standstill and stuck in a block of traffic.

4. The true soldier fights not because he hates what is in front of him, but because he loves what is behind him.

5. Without authority there is no liberty.

Conjunctions

Conjunctions connect words, phrases, or clauses together. Conjunctions may be found anywhere in a sentence, including at the beginning, but almost never at the end unless a sentence is interrupted or fading off.

The word FANBOYS will help you remember some common conjunctions.

The conjunctions For, And, Nor, But, Or, Yet, and So are often used to connect words, phrases, and clauses. Each of these conjunctions has a different meaning.

For—provides further explanation
And—indicates an addition
Nor—indicates an alternative that is negative
But—gives a contrast or exception
Or—provides another option
Yet—indicates a logical although contrary idea or option
So—indicates a consequence or result

Be aware of other functions of these words.

Examples: We were looking <u>for our lost dog</u>. ("For" is used as a preposition here.)

The room was <u>so disorganized</u> that we couldn't find a thing. ("So" is used as an adverb here.)

CHOOSING CONJUNCTIONS EXERCISE

Choose the conjunction (for, and, nor, but, or, yet, so) that best completes each sentence.

Example: We were late, ___*so*___ we began to hurry. (consequence)

1. We could visit the park _____ go to a movie. (option)

2. I would like to finish my math, _____ I must see who is calling. (contrary idea)

3. The children took care of horses _____ cows. (an addition)

4. A tornado warning sounded, _____ we went down to the basement. (consequence)

5. We were not afraid _____ were we worried when we heard the strange music coming from Chase's room. (a negative alternative)

6. We knew that he was practicing the accordion, _____ he had just had his first lesson. (further explanation)

7. We are leaving now, _____ we will return after lunch. (contrast)

Finding Conjunctions Exercise

In the two verses that follow, underline the common conjunctions. Remember FANBOYS. The first verse was written by Fr. Abram Joseph Ryan in reference to the defeat of the Confederate Army during the American Civil War. Look for six conjunctions in Fr. Ryan's poem. He uses the same two conjunctions several times.

1. Furl that Banner, for 'tis weary;

Round its staff 'tis drooping dreary;

  Furl it, fold it, it is best;

For there's not a man to wave it,

And there's not a sword to save it,

And there's no one left to lave it

In the blood that heroes gave it;

And its foes now scorn and brave it;

  Furl it, hide it—let it rest!

In this second verse by Joyce Kilmer about a battlefield during the first World War, look for seven conjunctions. Conjunctions are repeated.

2. In a wood they call the Rouge Bouquet

There is a new-made grave to-day,

Built by never a spade nor pick

Yet covered with earth ten metres thick.

There lie many fighting men,

  Dead in their youthful prime,

Never to laugh nor love again

  Nor taste the Summertime.

For Death came flying through the air

And stopped his flight at the dugout stair,

Touched his prey and left them there,

  Clay to clay.

Interjections

Interjections express emotion. They may be separate from the sentence or connected with a comma. If the interjection expresses extreme emotion, then an exclamation mark is used.

Example: No, I would rather not run ten miles in my bare feet. (a preference)

No! I forgot to study for my final exam. (extreme dismay)

Some common interjections are O or Oh, Wow, Ouch, Hurray, Hey, What, Eh, Um, and Alleluia.

Be careful not to overuse interjections. Few things are truly earth-shattering.

Frequently we hear God's Holy Name used as an interjection. When people use God's Name carelessly without intending to address or call upon Him earnestly, their words violate the second Commandment. We can easily understand why. We would not want anyone to use our name carelessly to show annoyance, anger, disgust, or surprise. We want others to respect our name.

USING INTERJECTIONS EXERCISE

Read the following aloud, stressing the underlined interjections based upon whether the interjection is separated from the main sentence or joined with a comma. The comments in the parentheses tell what is being expressed.

"Hey, who is that? Someone's attracting a crowd." (mild interest)

"I have no idea."

"Let's get a closer look."

"Sure!" (enthusiasm)

"Ouch!" (pain)

"Oh dear! I stepped on someone's toe." (anxiety)

"Sorry! I didn't mean to do that." (regret)

"Please look where you are going."

"I will, and I really am sorry."

"Well, that's okay." (mild or polite acceptance)

"What? It's a juggler." (surprise)

"Wow! He's really good." (delight)

Choosing Interjections Exercise

Based upon the comments in parenthesis, decide which interjection from the word bank to use.

Example: _Ugh!_ That stinks. (strong disgust)

1. _____ , I forgot to lock the front door. (mild annoyance)

2. _____ , that sounds like hail. (medium anxiety)

3. _____ Sing to Jesus! (strong devotion)

4. _____ my Lord! Have pity on me! (strong remorse)

5. _____ , do I want the chocolate ice cream or the vanilla? (mild uncertainty)

6. _____ Look at those fireworks! (strong excitement)

Word Bank

Um	O
Alleluia!	Oh no
Oh dear	Ah!

Review of Prepositions, Conjunctions and Interjections

Underline and label the prepositions (Prep), conjunctions (Con), and interjections (Inter) in the following verses by James Whitcomb Riley. The first excerpt is from "An Old Sweetheart of Mine."

<pre>
       Con Inter   Prep   Prep
</pre>

Example: <u>But</u>, <u>ah</u>! my dream is broken <u>by</u> a step <u>upon</u> the stair . . .

1. O Childhood-days enchanted! O the magic of the Spring!—

With all green boughs to blossom white, and all bluebirds to sing!

When all the air, to toss and quaff, made life a jubilee

And changed the children's song and laugh to shrieks of ecstasy.

This second verse is from "A Song of the Road"

2. Ho! I will walk with you, my lad,

Be weather black or blue

Or roadsides frost or dew, my lad—

O I will walk with you.

Gilbert Keith Chesterton (1874-1936), English author and convert to Catholicism. Chesterton is probably best known among Catholics for his brilliant and witty writing on a wide variety of topics, including apologetics and social conditions, and for the ever-popular *Father Brown* mystery series.

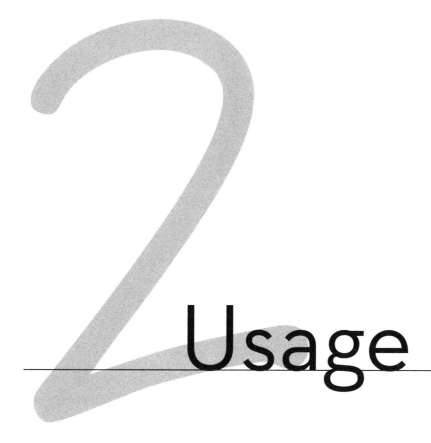

2 Usage

English usage is sometimes more than mere taste, judgment and education—sometimes it's sheer luck, like getting across the street. — E. B. White

Complex Sentences

We have looked at simple sentences, which are also called independent clauses, and compound sentences, which are two or more independent clauses joined together with proper punctuation. Now we will look at complex sentences.

A complex sentence is an independent clause with one or more dependent clauses. An independent clause can stand alone, but a dependent clause is not a complete thought.

However, writers use dependent clauses as adjectives, adverbs, and nouns. Sometimes a single adjective, adverb, or noun is not enough for the mature writer who then pulls out dependent clauses to express complex thoughts.

Example: I suppose [that] personal computers need little explanation, since they have become common necessities, which everyone expects to have access to.

In this example of a complex sentence, there are three dependent clauses. The independent clause is "I suppose that personal computers need little explanation." What is supposed? That personal computers need little explanation. The word *that* is bracketed because it may be omitted from the sentence. This dependent clause is the direct object of the verb. Thus it is used as a **noun** since direct objects are nouns—persons, places, things, or ideas.

The second dependent clause is "since they have become common necessities." This clause functions as an **adverb** because it indicates the reason or purpose for computers needing little explanation.

The third dependent clause is "which everyone expects to have access to," which is functioning as an **adjective** describing what kind of necessities computers are.

Subject-Verb Agreement

Verbs must agree in number with the subject. A plural subject needs a plural verb, and a singular subject needs a singular verb. Plural means more than one and singular means one. Therefore a plural subject is a subject referring to more than one person, place, thing, or idea. A singular subject refers to only one person, place, thing, or idea.

Plural subjects often end in s. However plural verbs do not usually end in s.

Singular subjects may end in s, and singular verbs may end in s.

Examples: The dogs <u>play</u>. The dog <u>plays</u>.
The dogs played. The dog played. (The past tense verb does not change.)
The dogs will play. The dog will play. (The future tense verb does not change.)

The men <u>sing</u>. The man <u>sings</u>.
The men sang. The man sang.
The men will sing. The man will sing.

The women <u>have</u> sung. The woman <u>has</u> sung. (The helping verb changes.)

Notice pronouns that do not fit the pattern:

I <u>sing</u>, not I sings.
We <u>sing</u>.
You <u>sing</u>. (both singular and plural)
They sing.
But . . . He <u>sings</u>, She <u>sings</u>, It <u>sings</u>.

I <u>am</u>, I <u>was</u>
We <u>are</u>, We <u>were</u>
You <u>are</u>, You <u>were</u> (both singular and plural)
He <u>is</u>, She <u>is</u>, It <u>is</u>, He <u>was</u>, She <u>was</u>, It <u>was</u>
They <u>are</u>, They <u>were</u>

U S A G E

SINGULAR OR PLURAL SUBJECTS EXERCISE

Label each sentence Sing if the subject and verb are singular and Pl if the subject and verb are plural.

Examples: _____PI_____ The horses are running in the field.

_____Sing_____ The Mass was held at midday. (Although Mass ends in s, it is one Mass and therefore singular.)

1. _____ It is a bright and sunny day in Epicuria.

2. _____ All the contestants have lined up for the pie throwing contest.

3. _____ The Queen and King of Epicuria can scarcely sit still on their thrones.

4. _____ They lean forward in order to see the contest better.

5. _____ The queen herself has entered a cherry pie in the contest.

6. _____ A contestant prepares to throw the first pie.

7. _____ The children stand ready to catch the pies.

8. _____ The king gives the signal and announces the flavor of pie to be thrown.

9. _____ With a strong arm, Mrs. Bess Jess throws a lemon meringue pie.

10. _____ Paul Potts catches the pie neatly and scampers off to share his prize with his friends.

11. _____ The crowd cheers because the entire pie has been saved, which is how pie throwing contests in Epicuria are judged.

Singular and Plural Verbs Exercise

Using the context of the sentence, write the correct **past tense** *form of the verb in each blank. The story is paraphrased from the gospel of Luke chapter 14.*

Example: You two _____*were*_____ already hard at work by eight this morning. (to be)

1. During one Sabbath, Jesus dined at the house of a Pharisee, and the guests

    _____ watching Him. (to be)

2. A man suffering from swollen legs _____ before Jesus. (to stand)

3. The lawyers and Pharisees _____ waiting silently. (to be)

4. And Jesus spoke, asking them if it _____ lawful to heal on the Sabbath. (to be)

5. They _____ not answer Him. (to do)

6. Jesus _____ the man, and the man left. (to heal)

7. If the men had _____ Jesus for healing the man, they would also have

    condemned themselves of hard-heartedness. (to condemn)

USAGE

Singular and Plural Subjects Exercise

Write a singular or plural pronoun as the subject based upon the verb used. Answers may vary.

Examples: <u>I/We/You/They</u> enjoy hiking in the early morning.

<u>He/She/It</u> does not sit idly by while others do the work.

1. Each evening, _____ pray the Rosary.

2. Mitchell stands up. Then _____ sings "So Long, Farewell" to us.

3. _____ am not ready for bed yet though.

4. _____ have to make a list of what will happen tomorrow.

5. Now _____ are all ready for bed.

6. Oh, no! _____ is beginning to thunder.

7. Rex! _____ have to sleep on your own bed.

8. _____ ignores our command and jumps in Theresa's bed.

9. _____ is happy to have a companion.

10. _____ fall asleep quickly in spite of the thunderstorm.

Collective Nouns

Sometimes deciding whether or not a subject is singular or plural takes extra thought.

Examples of Collective Nouns:

The <u>family</u> lives near the park. *The collective noun is used as a singular subject and takes a singular verb.*

The <u>grandparents</u> of the family live up the street. *The subject, grandparents, is plural (and not a collective noun) and takes a plural verb.*

The <u>classes</u> were dismissed. *Remember that collective nouns can be plural, as in this sentence.*

The <u>class</u> of history students was dismissed. *Here we have one class, although it has more than one student, that is dismissed.*

EDITING VERBS FOR COLLECTIVE NOUNS EXERCISE

If the subject and verb agree in number, then check the sentence as correct. If the subject and verb do not agree, then cross out the verb and write the correct form of the verb.

Examples: _____✓ The armies are marching.

_____ The army ~~are~~ *is* marching.

1. _____ The homeschoolers' Civil War history class is meeting at noon.

2. _____ When they cannot go outside, the Jenkins family dance in the living room.

3. _____ The small company sell handmade furniture.

4. _____ A raft of otters are floating belly up in the water.

5. _____ Flocks of geese are winging their way south.

6. _____ The pad of paper is on the desk.

7. _____ The teams meets today to compete for the annual trophy.

8. _____ The bouquets of flowers was scattered about the bedrooms.

9. _____ The public is asking for less corruption in government.

Indefinite Pronouns

*I*ndefinite pronouns require close attention. The writer must determine if the pronoun is referring to numbers of people, places, things, or ideas. If that is the case, then the indefinite pronoun will take a plural verb. If the pronoun is referring to an amount, then the verb will be singular.

Examples:

One-third of the <u>pizza</u> is missing. *We are thinking of the fractional amount of one pizza and so use a singular verb.*

One-third of the <u>pies</u> are frozen solid. *Here we are considering the fractional amounts of numbers of pies and use a plural verb.*

All [of the people, of the children, of the party-goers] dance. *Numbers of people are dancing, so we use the plural verb.*

However, all of the catsup is on the floor. *The whole amount of catsup is on the floor. We are thinking of the catsup as one big mess on the floor.*

Many are happy. *Many indicates a number of people or other objects.*

Less [effort, energy, time] is required. *Less is used as a single quantity or amount.*

Few [people, dogs, Americans] enjoy spicy foods for breakfast.

Everyone sings. Everybody applauds. *The "one" in everyone is a clue that you will use a singular verb.*

None of the fruit is ripe. *Not one piece of fruit is ripe.*

Almost none of the cars made are bright orange. *Very few of the number of cars made are bright orange.*

EDITING VERBS FOR INDEFINITE PRONOUNS EXERCISE

If the subject and verb agree in number, then check the sentence. If the subject and verb do not agree, then cross out the verb and write the correct form of the verb.

Example: _____ Much ~~are~~ *is* expected of the superb athletes.

1. _____ Half of the cookies is baked and ready to eat.

2. _____ Somebody is calling us long distance.

3. _____ Most of my chocolate bunny is still uneaten.

4. _____ Each of the men have at least one son and one daughter.

5. _____ None of the dogs is wearing a collar. (Not one of the dogs . . .)

6. _____ Almost none of the cats sleep on top of the computer.

7. _____ All of the cabbage and potato hash are eaten.

8. _____ Neither child are responsible for the muddy footprints.

9. _____ Some of the mud were left outside where it belongs.

10. _____ Some of you are hoping to learn to drive soon.

USAGE

Review of Indefinite Pronouns

Underline the indefinite pronouns and indicate whether the pronouns are singular or plural. The italicized verbs will help you recognize singular and plural pronouns because a singular pronoun must have a singular verb and a plural pronoun requires a plural verb.

Examples: ___Sing___ <u>None</u> of the birthday cake *was* left on the plate.
Only one cake was on the plate.

___Pl___ <u>Some</u> of the children in the library *whisper* if they have a question.
Notice that "whisper" does not refer to "library" but to "the children."

1. _____ Most of the book *contains* nothing but photographs.

2. _____ More *are arriving* daily.

3. _____ During the circus, everyone *laughs* when the clowns appear.

4. _____ Everybody in the house *is* busy with chores.

5. _____ All of the drivers *stop* when the ducks cross the road to reach the river.

6. _____ By the end of spring, all of the forest of maple trees *has become* lively and green.

7. _____ In the evening around seven o'clock, many *walk* along the lake for exercise.

8. _____ Few *fly* kites in the winter or during thunderstorms.

9. _____ Less of their time *is spent* in front of the television now that they are learning to kayak.

10. _____ Although both boys enjoy walking, neither *wants* to hike up the mountain in the dark. (Two boys like to walk, but when "neither" is the subject of a sentence, it takes the singular form. Is "neither" the subject of this sentence?)

11. _____ Several of the parents who donated money to our picnic also *volunteered* their time. (Two prepositional phrases and the clause "who were donating money" separate the indefinite pronoun from its verb.)

Review of Subject–Verb Agreement

On your own paper, write and identify the verbs as singular or plural in this excerpt from E.B. White's 1955 essay "Home-Coming." Include any helping verbs and linking verbs.

Familiarity is the thing—the sense of belonging. It grants exemption from all evil, all shabbiness. A farmer pauses in the doorway of his barn and he is wearing the right boots. A sheep stands under an apple tree and it wears the right look, and the tree is hung with puckered frozen fruit of the right color. The spruce boughs that bank the foundations of the homes keep out the only true winter wind, and the light that leaves the sky at four o'clock automatically turns on the yellow lamps within, revealing to the soft-minded motorist interiors of perfect security, kitchens full of a just and lasting peace. (Or so it seems to the homing traveler.)

Troublesome Words

Many of us commonly misuse words, and so what you hear frequently may not always be correct. It may sound correct, but grammatically speaking, it isn't. Let's look at some of these troublesome words.

LAY OR LIE?

The key to knowing when to use lay or lie is understanding the tense.

Lay requires an object when it is used as a present tense verb.
Use **lay** when you mean to **place** something.
You may wish to **lay** your **head** on this soft pillow. A hen **lays eggs**.

Thus a hen may settle down to **lay** an egg, but she will not **lie** an egg.
People and chickens may **lay** down in the past tense, as in "We **lay** down yesterday for a long nap." However, we may not lay down now. We must instead **lie** down at the present time.

Use **lie** to mean **recline** in the present tense.
Lie may take an adverb or prepositional phrase, as in "I **lie** in the hammock every day."

In the present tense, you may not **lay** in the hammock, in bed, or on the sofa because you are not a chicken. If you try to lay in the hammock, in bed, or on the sofa and are successful at laying, then please remember to put any eggs you lay into the refrigerator.

Here are the forms:

Present Tense	Past Tense	Past Participle
lie, lies	lay	lain
lay, lays	laid	laid

The tricky part is remembering that in the past tense **lay** takes the meaning to recline or rest, and **laid** means to place or put. So it is perfectly all right if yesterday you **lay** in the hammock and read a novel.

USAGE

Lay chanting exercise

Say each perfectly correct present tense sentence aloud three times.

I lay the books on the table.

You lay the books on the table.

He lays the books on the table.

She lays the books on the table.

We lay the books on the table.

They lay the books on the table.

Objects for lay exercise

Write an object for each present tense sentence.

Example: Fr. Thomas lays the _____*paten*_____ on the altar.

1. The ostriches lay many _____ .

2. The students lay the _____ on the desk.

3. The firefighter lays the _____ down.

4. At the end of a long day, I lay my _____ off the end of the couch, much to

   everyone else's annoyance.

5. Between bites, we lay our _____ down and chew our food thoroughly.

6. You always lay your _____ on the shelf.

7. The puppy lays its _____ on the windowsill and barks at a squirrel.

U S A G E

Lie Chanting Exercise

Say each perfectly correct present tense sentence aloud three times.

I lie down.

You lie down.

She lies down.

He lies down.

It lies down.

We lie down.

They lie down.

Choosing Lay or Lie Exercise

Write either lay, lays, lie, or lies in the blank to form a grammatically correct sentence.

Example: I ___*lie*___ in the hammock every day to read.

1. The painter _____ down the palette and paintbrush.

2. I should _____ my sunglasses out of reach of the baby.

3. We are so tired that we could _____ down and sleep the rest of the afternoon.

4. Do you want to _____ the fish on the grill now?

5. Gently and carefully, Father _____ the baby in her crib.

6. Is he going to _____ on the floor to assemble the puzzle?

7. During his vacation, he _____ on the beach all day.

8. Please _____ the thick towels within easy reach of the swimmers.

More Chanting Exercises

Say each sentence aloud three times.

Present Progressive:

I am laying the books on the table.

You are laying the books on the table.

He is laying the books on the table.

We are laying the books on the table.

They are laying the books on the table.

The table is now covered with books!

Present Progressive:

I am lying on the sofa.

You are lying on the sofa.

She is lying on the sofa.

It is lying on the sofa.

We are lying on the sofa.

They are lying on the sofa.

It's a very large sofa!

Past Tense:

Yesterday I lay down for a nap.

Yesterday you lay down for a nap.

Yesterday he lay down for a nap.

Yesterday she lay down for a nap.

Yesterday it lay down for a nap.

Yesterday we lay down for a nap.

Yesterday they lay down for a nap.

Yesterday everyone lay down for a nap and snored loudly.

More Troublesome Words and How to Use Them Properly

All right is okay as long as you write it as two words.
They were feeling **all right**.

Alternate means every other one or a substitute. **Alternative** refers to a choice or option.
The chess club competes on **alternate** Saturdays. They meet every other Saturday.
Teri was named as an **alternate** in case one of the other chess club members could not make the tournament.
Because I am busy every other Saturday, my **alternative** was to join the skydiving club.

Can means being able. Do not substitute it for **may**, which indicates permission or possibility.
May we bring lemonade in glass bottles onto the beach? Yes, you **may** if you are strong enough to carry them. We **can** carry the glass bottles because they are not too heavy.

Care less requires careful handling, so do not be careless with its usage. "I could **not care less**" means that I do not mind. "I could **care less**" logically means what? I will try to **care less**, I care a little bit, or I'm just being careless with the language?

Different from is the correct form because things differ from one another. Avoid using **different than**. The taste of their homemade spaghetti sauce is deliciously **different from** the taste of canned sauce.

Each and everyone should be avoided as being redundant. Choose one or the other and say what you have to say. **Each** of us should learn to speak and write correctly. **Everyone** should speak and write correctly.

The **effect** of using **effect** incorrectly **affects** us all. **Affect** means to influence. His speech about Shakespeare's villains **affected** us dramatically. **Effect** may be used as a noun to mean result. A sudden boom of thunder often creates the **effect** of trembling in my dog. **Effect** works as a verb to mean to bring about. A thunderstorm usually **effects** a change in the humidity.

Farther refers to physical distance. **Further** indicates time or quantity. Suzie can pitch a horseshoe **farther** than her brother can pitch one. I would like the time to do **further** research before making a decision.

Using the adverbs **Firstly**, **Secondly** and **Thirdly** is not the best way to distinguish your points. Either create a numbered list or write **first, second, third**. When writing **first, second**, and **third**, count your points to make sure that your second point is not actually the third point.

Imply indicates that something is suggested but not specifically expressed. **Infer** means that a conclusion has been reached based upon the evidence. The salesman **implied** that the

SuperHybrid was not as effective as the more expensive HyperHybrid. Using historical data, the scholar **inferred** that Shakespeare was Catholic.

Importantly should be avoided because the sentence will be stronger and less pretentious by using a more precise term. Instead of writing "Most **importantly**, we shut the gates before the cows got out," write "We wisely shut the gates before the cows got out."

Irregardless is not a word **regardless** of what you may have heard. The negative suffix –less is sufficient. Do not create a double negative by attaching the negative prefix ir-.

Less is not a substitute for **fewer** because **less** indicates quantity and **fewer** indicates number. We worked **fewer** hours today than we did yesterday. Please use **less** detergent so that the suds do not overflow onto the floor. When used as a subject, **less** takes the singular verb. **Less** butter **is** better. **Fewer** requires a plural verb: **fewer** people **are** eating out now.

Like is overused and misused. Instead of saying and writing, "I was **like** so happy," let's clear the air of word pollution and simply say or write "I was thrilled, I was delighted, I was ecstatic."

In addition, use **like** correctly as a preposition to show relationship, but never as a conjunction. **Like** a river, the spilled milked flowed off the table and onto the floor. But not "He hung on to the string of the deflated balloon **like** it might still float off." Instead revise to "He hung on to the string of the deflated balloon **as if** it might still float off."

One of the best, happiest, most exciting is an easy but meaningless way to begin a topic. Why? You are immediately making a judgment for the reader or listener. Present the information and let the reader or listener make a judgment. Many, many essays begin with a version of this phrase, and the result is that progress is stopped. "It was one of the **happiest** summers of my life" already sums up the topic. "Last summer, I flew to Epicuria by myself. Everyone in Epicuria speaks English, so I wasn't nervous about communicating. I had dreamed of flying to this tiny country whose motto was 'Real food takes thyme.' I had been invited to meet the King and Queen of Epicuria and to have lunch with them. I clutched my invitation as if culinary thugs might wrestle me for possession of it." Yes, this takes more thought and more time, but your reader will enjoy it far more than your immediate declaration that it was the most exciting summer of your life. By the end of your essay, you will not need to make this judgment because your reader will have inferred it if you give enough details.

Split infinitives refer to infinitives that are separated by an adverb. To greedily eat, to pompously walk, and to gently touch are examples of split infinitives. Infinitives in many other languages cannot be split because they are one word, but English infinitives require two words. Generally, we try to avoid splitting infinitives in writing. You may avoid split infinitives by using strong verbs to express your meaning—**to gobble, to strut, to caress**. If you can't find a stronger verb, then position the adverb after the verb, as in **to hope wistfully, to strum the guitar softly**.

Then or **Than**? **Then** refers to time. This happened and **then** that happened later. **Than** is used to compare. It looks more like an eagle **than** like a goose. Nevertheless, remember that an eagle differs **from** a goose; it is not different **than** a goose.

They, **their**, **he**, or **she**? Because of gender neutral trends, the plural pronoun **they** is frequently, yet incorrectly, used after singular indefinite pronouns. Everyone is sure **they** are going to win? No, use **he** or **she**. If a female is speaking of herself or primarily to females, she should use **she**. The same holds true for a male; he may use **he** grammatically correctly when referring to himself or speaking to a group of mostly males. When the group is mixed, avoid singular indefinite pronouns and rely on gender neutral plurals. Eloquent **speakers** are sure to hold the attention of **their** audience. **All** of **us** were pleased because **we** knew how to divide the toys fairly among the whole group. In addition, you may use the second person pronoun **you** if you are addressing a crowd or the reader. **You** may now leave the stadium silently. Reader, **you** may want to review this information before the quiz.

Use an infinitive with **try**. The writer must **try to avoid** offending readers, rather than the writer must **try and avoid** offending readers. Using the conjunction *and* seems to indicate the writer is performing two actions instead of one.

Very should be used sparingly. Try to use strong adjectives and adverbs to eliminate the need for **very**. "The night was **very** dark" may come easily to mind, but think the situation through further. "The night grew dark and then darker as the clouds covered the moon and stars." "We **very** willingly helped with the barbeque" can be revised to "Eagerly *or* Enthusiastically, we helped with the barbeque."

DELETING TROUBLESOME WORDS EXERCISE

Cross out sentences that contain the incorrect use of words or phrases.

Example: The rhinoceros must try to escape the hunters. ~~The rhinoceros must try and escape the hunters~~.

1. If you want to be content in life, than you will practice charity. If you want to be content in life,

    then you will practice charity.

2. To quickly catch the thief was their main goal. To catch the thief quickly was their main goal.

3. The sick children would soon be all right because they received loving attention from their

    family. The sick children would soon be alright because they received loving attention from their

    family.

4. The athlete was a very fast runner. The athlete was a swift runner.

5. The crowd inferred that the play had been cancelled when they could not open the doors to the auditorium. The crowd implied that the play had been cancelled when they could not open the doors to the auditorium.

6. Sudden fame had a ruinous affect upon her. Sudden fame had a ruinous effect upon her.

7. The habits of a rat are different than those of a gerbil. The habits of a rat are different from those of a gerbil.

8. Each ballerina found her dancing costume ready to wear because the staff had worked overtime. Each ballerina found their dancing costume ready to wear because the staff had worked overtime.

9. The essays were well written like all essays should be. The essays were well written as all essays should be.

10. Less than half the city is receiving rain. Less than half the city are receiving rain.

11. Few of the books in their collection are leather bound. Few of the books in their collection is leather bound.

Choosing Grammatically Correct Words Exercise

Write the grammatically correct word from the choices given in the blanks to complete each sentence.

Example: He sang _____*like*_____ a professional. (like, as)

1. The Davises serve ice cream to their guests _____ of the outside temperature. (irregardless, regardless)

2. _____ , the sun provides us with light and heat, and psychologically, sunshine lifts our spirits. (Importantly, Physically)

3. Could you _____ that a cloudy day might tempt us to be grumpy? (imply, infer)

4. _____ are complaining about the traffic now that the road has been widened. (Fewer, Less)

5. I have _____ than ten items, so I will use the speedy checkout. (fewer, less)

6. Everybody is remarking that _____ electric razor is defective. (their, his)

7. The Campos family drove _____ than they had planned. (further, farther)

8. _____ , the solution should be weighed before performing the experiment. (Firstly, First)

9. _____ we make finger food for supper tonight so that the cleaning up will be easier? (May, Can)

10. If you _____ hike for three hours, then you will enjoy taking this trail. (may, can)

11. Does the use of _____ fuels make a positive difference in the environment? (alternate, alternative)

12. By visiting the library, we can research this question _____ . (farther, further)

U S A G E

Diagramming Sentences

We diagram sentences to show how the parts work together. Now we use our knowledge of subjects, predicates, adjectives, adverbs, dependent clauses, direct objects, and so on to see the big picture of the sentence.

Begin diagramming by determining the simple subject and the simple predicate.

Shakespeare is writing.

The simple subject and simple predicate rest on a horizontal (lying down) line. They are separated by a vertical (standing up) line that cuts the horizontal line into two parts.

We rarely write such simple sentences. What is Shakespeare writing? If he is writing a play, then *play* is the **direct object and part of the simple predicate**. Thus the vertical line separating a direct object does not cross the horizontal line.

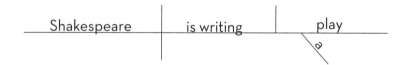

If we added an adjective to our sentence, where would it go? Adjectives are placed on slanted lines that branch off from the noun or pronoun they are modifying.

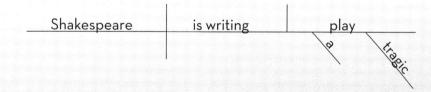

USAGE

DIAGRAMMING EXERCISE

On your own paper, diagram these sentences. (If using different colors appeals to you, then use colored pencils. Choose a different color for each part of speech. For example, nouns can be blue, adjectives green, verbs red, adverbs orange, and prepositions brown.)

1. The crowd was shouting.

2. Shakespeare rented a house.

3. Emily Forli baked bread.

4. The student borrowed a red pen.

5. The happy clown clapped her hands.

Predicate Nouns and Adjectives

In the sentence, *The writer is an American*, *American* is not the direct object, but it is part of the simple predicate. It is the predicate noun, which we diagram in this way:

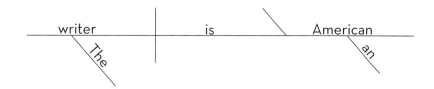

The predicate adjective *blue* in the sentence, *The pen is blue*, would be diagrammed with a slanted line also. The slanted line will not cross the horizontal line.

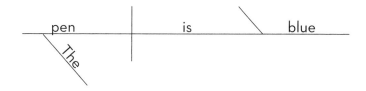

Because predicate nouns and predicate adjectives refer to the subject, the line is slanted toward the subject.

DIAGRAMMING PREDICATE NOUNS AND PREDICATE ADJECTIVES EXERCISE

On your own paper, diagram these sentences.

1. I am her mother.

2. The children are friends.

3. The pizza had been too hot. (*Too* is an adverb modifying *hot*, so it will branch off below *hot*.)

4. That swimmer is famous.

5. The excited children were close friends.

USAGE

Compound Subjects and Predicates

What if Emily Forli and her mother baked bread and ate it? We would have a compound subject and a compound predicate.

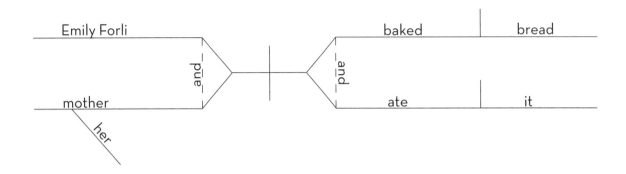

What would you do if the Queen and King [of Epicuria] had been walking and talking?

DIAGRAMMING COMPOUND SUBJECTS AND COMPOUND PREDICATES EXERCISE

On your own paper, diagram these sentences.

1. Latin and Greek are foreign languages.

2. The students were eating and studying.

3. Thomas and Hope have been writing and have completed their assignment.

4. Carlos and Marie wrote sentences and read stories.

Elwyn Brooks White (1899-1985), American author and essayist best known for his witty essays in *The New Yorker* magazine and the children's story *Charlotte's Web*. This popular story has a strong pro-life basis. Although White's parents were Christian, he did not claim to belong to any particular denomination. White was greatly admired for his skill by his fellow writers. He wrote about small homely incidents and international affairs, and in one essay "Here is New York," he mentions the vulnerability of the city to an aerial attack. White's essays and books are not available on the Web because they are protected by copyright.

3 Mechanics

The mechanics of writing may seem like a goblin trying to get you, but these nuts and bolts are necessary to writing so that we can be understood. Following the technical elements of writing does require that we watch out. Watch out for the sake of your reader and for the sake of what you wish to say.

Capitalization

Capital letters emphasize words. The word capital itself is from a Latin word meaning "head," and the head of anything is significant. Use capital letters to emphasize words that should be emphasized, such as names, personal titles, the first letter of the first word of sentences, the pronoun "I," and the important words in titles. We also capitalize names we use in relationships under certain conditions.

First Letters of Sentences and of Each Line of a Poem:
> **When** he is a little chap,
> **We** call him *Nap.*
> **When** he somewhat older grows,
> **We** call him *Doze.*
> **When** his age by hours we number,
> **We** call him *Slumber.*
> — Fr. John Banister Tabb

Proper Nouns:
Elizabeth Anne Perpetua Beaumont is her full name.

She visited **Saint Patrick's Cathedral** in **New York City** to hear an organ recital.

They live on the **West Coast** now, but they used to live in **New England.**

Proper nouns name specific people, places, or things.
The following sentence contains no proper nouns: The man traveled south to the city to visit a cathedral.

Pronouns:
If you would like my help, **I** would be happy to assist you.

The pronoun I is capitalized probably for aesthetic reasons, as it is an insignificant letter all by itself and apt to get lost in print.

Personal Titles:
Doctor Martin, **Father** Brown, **Inspector** Alleyn, **General** Dolittle, **Mrs.** Beacon

Literary, Film, Television, and Artistic Titles:
The first letters of the first word, the last word, and other important words are capitalized.

The Passion of the Christ is the name of a movie.

"Daily Sing to Mary" is the hymn we like to sing.

We bought a print of a painting called ***The Boating Party.***

The World Over with Raymond Arroyo is a popular television program on EWTN.

Divinity:
We often capitalize pronouns, names, and titles referring to God, as in the prayer "O **Holy Spirit**, **You** are the **Third Person** of the **Holy Trinity**."

Although Mary is not divine, out of respect, we capitalize titles referring to her but not pronouns referring to her unless those pronouns begin a sentence or are part of a title.

Mary, **Seat of Wisdom**, pray for us.

Relationships:
When the relationship is used as a title or name, then capitalize it.

Is it time to pick strawberries, **Mom**?
My mom is taking us to pick strawberries.
That man is **Uncle Homer**.
His uncle works at the dairy.
Grandfather Maurice likes to swim.
He swims with other men who are also grandfathers.

READING CAPITAL LETTERS ALOUD EXERCISE

Pay attention to when and where capitals are used by reading them aloud.

Example: Marcy enjoys reading the best-selling book *The Many Delights of Desserts in Epicuria.* Say aloud "Marcy, Capital M, enjoys reading the best-selling book *The,* Capital T, *Many,* Capital M, *Delights,* Capital D, *of Desserts,* Capital D, *in Epicuria,* Capital E.

1. In Epicuria, Princess Cecilia studies grammar on Tuesdays and Thursdays.

2. On Sundays, the royal family attends Holy Mass and then enjoys a picnic at Sweetwood Park.

3. Prince Alfred studies his favorite cookbook, *The Grilling of Meat.*

4. Prince Almanzo rides his horse, Marco Polo, in the afternoons.

5. What is the Princess Catherine doing in her grandfather's study?

6. She is reading to Grandmother Eugenia and to her mother from the Bible.

7. The new chef from South America appears and announces, "I have prepared tea and hot chocolate."

8. Suddenly, all the princes and princesses flood into the study of the Chateau de Cheddar for refreshments.

Capitalizing Exercise

Indicate why the bold-faced words were capitalized: first letter [of a sentence], first letter of each line [of a poem], personal title, title of a work, relationship, divinity, proper noun, pronoun I.

Examples: _____*pronoun I*_____ When **I** tried to serve the ice cream, the scoop went flying across the room.

_____*proper noun*_____ Every **Wednesday,** we have a test.

1. _____ Out of the depths, have I cried to **Thee.**

2. _____ "**Is** skimming o'er a stagnant pool/ **Your** only occupation?" —Tabb

3. _____ Over there is the **Archbishop of Epicuria.**

4. _____ You and **I** should greet him.

5. _____ Thomas is reading "**Little Orphant Annie**" written by James Whitcomb Riley.

6. _____ **Edmund Clerihew Bentley** invented the clerihew, a comical four-line poem, when he was only sixteen years old.

7. _____ The Mertons went to visit **Aunt Polly** in the country.

8. _____ Aunt Polly lives in **West Chester Township.**

9. _____ **Our Lady, Star of the Sea,** pray for us.

10. _____ He sailed west across the **Pacific.**

Commas

If you are dropping commas only when you want your reader to take a breath, please keep breathing. Commas are not about pausing to breathe although you do not want your reader to run out of breath.

Commas mean serious business. They allow us to write perfectly understandable sentences, especially when we are listing more than two items.

For example, if you wish to list more than two grains, you will require the services of the **serial comma.**

Example: The farmers are growing rye, wheat, oats, and corn.

Sometimes, the last comma is omitted in a series. "The people cheered, shouted and danced in the streets." This omission may lead to confusion, as in "We searched for brownish reds, pale blue grays and whites." Were the whites we wanted pale blue whites? For the sake of clarity, write "We searched for brownish reds, pale blue grays, and whites."

Is this sentence clear? "Frances and Mark, Tom and Carol and John and Mary were the couples we wanted to see dance first." It looks awkward because Tom and Carol and John and Mary are a quartet instead of a couple. "Frances and Mark, Tom and Carol, and John and Mary were the couples."

When we punctuate, we are helping the reader understand units of meaning, so place those commas carefully for maximum comprehension.

READING COMMAS EXERCISE

Read the commas aloud in these sentences.

Example: "The alligators, comma the kangaroos, comma the giraffes, comma and the zebras were all sleeping.

1. Find the apostrophes, question marks, periods, and commas on the keyboard.

2. The girls' bicycles were dark red, light red, and hot pink.

3. The woman's hat was composed of feathers, felt, ribbons, and beads.

4. We cooked hotdogs, ate them, and watched a movie.

5. Mary sang, Bob played the piano, and their parents clapped.

6. Zoe's, Kelly's, and Francesca's dogs all began to bark at midnight.

Using Commas Correctly Exercise

Write "Correct" if **all** *the commas are used correctly. Write "Incorrect" if a comma is missing or in the wrong place.*

1. _____ Doris and I met Kim, John, and Marie for breakfast, went to Mark's for lunch, and ate supper with our parents.

2. _____ The babies were wrapped in pink white, and yellow blankets.

3. _____ We ate shrimp, oysters, clams, and fish from the seafood buffet.

4. _____ The duets were sung by Jeff and Diane, Richard and Marie, and Kelly and Davis.

5. _____ We bought green, onions, yellow, squash, red, cabbage, and orange, peppers for the meal.

6. _____ The costume designer drew three kinds of coats—gold and silver white and pink and yellow and blue.

7. _____ The Dicksons the Carvers and the Washingtons all play the piano beautifully.

8. _____ Haley takes music lessons, swimming lessons, and etiquette lessons from Mr. Parks, Mrs. Mullins, and Miss Finley.

MECHANICS

More Uses for Commas

Commas are also used in direct address to set off names:
Father Brown, are you well?
Yes, Mrs. Clarke, we would be happy to help you.

Commas are used with appositives:
Lily Jo, my goddaughter, has sent me a letter.
Girl with a Watering Can, a painting by Renoir, is an example of Impressionism, a style of painting.

Commas are used in quotations:
They said, "We read the news online."
"Then we looked at the weather forecast," they added.
"Of course," they pointed out, "we also listened to the radio for local information."
"How do you get your news?" they wondered.

Notice the position of the comma outside the quotations marks in the first sentence and inside the quotation marks in the second sentence. Notice both commas in the third sentence. Notice that the question mark is not followed by a comma. Exclamation marks are also not followed by commas.

WRITING COMMAS EXERCISE

Rewrite the sentences, adding commas where necessary.

Example: She asked "Edgar are you going to mow the grass?"

She asked, "Edgar, are you going to mow the grass?"

1. "Yes Caroline" Edgar replied "I plan to mow the grass wash the windows and trim the shrubs."

2. The Yard Machine a recent purchase from the home improvement store would not start.

3. "Caroline the mower isn't working!"

4. Edgar gave the mower one last try sighed deeply and looked about for a bucket.

5. He found a yellow bucket a plastic object with a large hole in the bottom.

6. "You can't possibly use that to wash the windows" Caroline said.

7. She added "Edgar I noticed that some birds are nesting in the shrubs."

8. Edgar decided that he would take the mower in for repairs purchase a sturdy new bucket and enjoy the sight of the nesting birds.

Parenthetic Expressions and Restrictive Clauses

But wait, commas can do even more work. They can set off parenthetic expressions. What is a parenthetic expression? It has nothing to do with parents. A parenthetic expression is an interruption that explains or comments upon the main sentence. Parenthetic expressions are not necessary to understand the meaning of the sentence. They are also referred to as **nonrestrictive clauses or phrases**. (A clause contains a subject and a verb, but a phrase does not.)

Examples of Parenthetic Expressions:

The rhinoceros is such an intriguing animal, <u>don't you think</u>?

Many years ago, <u>long before you and I were born,</u> lived a Spanish princess who married a French prince.

Examples of Restrictive Clauses and Phrases:

The men <u>standing at the corner</u> were splashed with mud.

People <u>who live in lighthouses</u> enjoy wonderful views of the coast.

These sentences do not contain commas because the phrase *standing at the corner* is required to understand the sentence and the clause *who live in lighthouses* is not an interruption but a necessary part of the sentence.

READING NONRESTRICTIVE AND RESTRICTIVE PHRASES AND CLAUSES EXERCISE

Read the sentences aloud, paying attention to the use of commas.

Example: The butler, comma who was married to the chauffeur's daughter, comma was impeccably dressed.

1. Fred and August Duesenberg, *two brothers who lived in Iowa,* taught themselves to build racing bicycles and then racing cars.

2. Their claim to fame was the expensive, fast, and elegant Duesenberg Model J, *a car which only the very rich could afford.*

MECHANICS

121

3. Most people *living in the 1930s* were astounded by the horsepower of the supercharged Duesenbergs, *which boasted a top speed of 140 miles per hour.*

4. *Offered to the public in 1932,* the Model B Ford cost about $500 and featured a front grille *that mimicked the Duesenberg grille.*

5. The winner of the 1921 French Grand Prix, *which was first run in 1906,* was driving a Duesenberg.

6. The Auburn Cord Duesenberg Automobile Museum building, *boasting an art-deco interior and fourteen plate-glass windows,* was once the headquarters and showroom of Duesenbergs.

MECHANICS

Commas and Conjunctions

Commas continue working hard to separate dependent clauses and independent clauses with the help of conjunctions.

Examples:

Although we can't afford a Duesenberg, we enjoy photographing these elegant and antique cars.
We enjoy photographing the elegant and antique Duesenbergs *although we can't afford these cars.*

When it appears at the **beginning** of a sentence, the dependent clause cannot stand alone, but it can be joined to an independent clause with the assistance of a comma. The dependent clause does not usually require a comma when it is placed at the **end** of a sentence.

The last Model T rolled off the assembly line in 1927, *and the Ford family stopped producing cars for a while as they worked on the next model.*

A comma alone is not enough to join together two independent clauses. The comma must be helped with a conjunction, such as for, and, nor, but, or, yet, and so.

USING COMMAS WITH DEPENDENT AND INDEPENDENT CLAUSES EXERCISE

Rewrite the sentences, placing a comma after a dependent clause and a comma and a conjunction between independent clauses.

Example: Crowds gathered to watch the antique car show they stood patiently as the announcer described each beautifully restored vehicle.

Crowds gathered to watch the antique car show, and they stood patiently as the announcer described each beautifully restored vehicle.

1. When the steam engine was invented people tried various methods of designing the first horseless carriage.

2. The usefulness of self-propelled cars was evident the question of how to invent a reliable everyday car remained.

3. Europeans in the 1890s were driving cars designed by Benz and Daimler Americans could buy Duryea and Winton automobiles.

4. Although steam, electricity, and gasoline were all options for powering cars gasoline cars became more popular because they could travel farther.

5. People had different reasons for buying cars not everyone who wanted a car could afford one.

6. Because cars had to be made by hand at first they were symbols of status for the wealthy.

7. Henry Ford lowered the price of automobiles by introducing new manufacturing techniques these techniques made the Model T affordable to many more people.

Review of Commas

If the commas are used correctly, place a ✓ in the blank.

Example: ___✓___ The March family, all ten of them, climbed into their van and drove to church.

1. _____ People have traveled by many means: foot, horse, boat, hot-air balloon, train, bus, plane, and spaceship.

2. _____ Although I have never ridden in a hot-air balloon, I would like to go to the Albuquerque International Balloon Fiesta.

3. _____ The bus leaves at seven in the morning, and the train leaves half an hour later.

4. _____ The airplane, which was piloted by her uncle, was a Cessna Skyhawk.

5. _____ Because of the expense, danger, and rigorous physical requirements, few people have traveled in space.

6. _____ "Courage is being scared to death," said John Wayne, "but saddling up anyway."

7. _____ Hohensalzburg Castle in Austria has a funicular railway, the Reiszug, which was opened around 1504 to carry supplies up to the castle.

8. _____ The Reiszug is an antique, but the ancient Greeks created a human- and animal-powered railway called the Diolkos to drag ships across a narrow stretch of land from the Gulf of Corinth to the Saronic Gulf.

9. _____ Many people complain about the hardships of traveling, yet we continue to travel, using whatever means we find available and affordable.

Semicolons and Colons

Is a semicolon half of a colon? You decide. The semicolon and colon are located on the same key of a computer keyboard. The semicolon has a dot and a comma, while the colon is two dots, one over the other.

The semicolon is more powerful than a comma. A semicolon *can* join two independent clauses together without the assistance of a conjunction. The clauses should be closely connected in content.

The Queen of Epicuria is napping; everyone is whispering until she wakes up.

The semicolon is considered formal; as a tuxedo is to fashion, so is the semicolon to grammar.

The semicolon may also be used with commas to separate elements in a list:

We have lunched in Paris, France, Paris, Texas, Moscow, Russia, Moscow, Texas, Houston, British Columbia, and Houston, Texas.

Yes, this is confusing, isn't it? Let's try this sentence again, using semicolons:

We have lunched in Paris, France; Paris, Texas; Moscow, Russia; Moscow, Texas; Houston, British Columbia; and Houston, Texas.

Now the meaning is easier to comprehend. There is a Paris, France and a Paris, Texas, and so on, and we have lunched in six places rather than in twelve.

READING SEMICOLONS EXERCISE

Read the sentences, including the semicolons and comma aloud.

1. The King and Queen of Epicuria were talking with the princes and princesses; their children were trying to persuade the King and Queen to increase their allowance.

2. "How much allowance do the royal children in London, England; Brussels, Belgium; Fredensborg, Denmark; and Stockholm, Sweden receive?" the King asked.

3. Prince Almanzo scratched his head; he had no idea as he had not recently texted any of them.

4. Princess Cecilia and Prince Alfred knew the answer; they didn't know how to convert the British pound, the Swedish krona, the Danish krone, and the Belgian euro to the basil, which was the national currency of Epicuria.

5. Princess Catherine pulled out her calculator; she entered a few numbers and groaned.

6. "According to my calculations, after converting all these currencies, we already get more allowance in basils than the other royal children do; I think I know the answer to our question," she said.

7. The Queen smiled to her husband, "My dear, we have such intelligent children, don't we?"

8. "Yes, and as it is the servants' day off, we can all roll up our sleeves; we have lunch to prepare," he replied. "Who wants Epicurian hamburgers?"

MECHANICS

More Colons

Colons are used more frequently than semicolons. We use a colon after an independent clause to list items, appositives, and quotations.

List—The 1933 Duesenberg featured several distinctive elements: a convertible top, a polished beltline, an eight-cylinder engine, and a gleaming coat of silver paint.

Appositive—Although the Duesenberg brothers enjoyed designing cars, their enjoyment was diminished by one thing: a lack of sales.

Quotation—The Duesenberg ads were simple: "He drives a Duesenberg."

We also use colons after the greeting in formal letters, to distinguish between hours and minutes and Bible chapters and verses, and to separate main titles from subtitles.

Examples:

Dear Madam:

10:57 p.m.

Psalm 8:2

Creative Communications: Thirty Writing, Speaking, and Drawing Projects for Homeschoolers

Using colons exercise

Add colons only if necessary to punctuate the sentences properly.

Example: The train leaves at 9 : 10 a.m., and I will want to take __ my hat, gloves, and raincoat. (*The first blank requires a colon, but the second does not, so the second blank is left empty.*)

1. Marjorie McMillan had memorized the following Bible verses__ Matthew 7__7, Mark 13__32, and

    Malachi 1__6.

2. Misty Moore's favorite foods are __ mushrooms, melons, and mangos.

3. Miriam Mitchell wrote lovely thank you letters, which all included the same sentiments first expressed by E.B. White_ "You have been my friend. That in itself is a tremendous thing."

4. Hi Muriel_

5. Dear Reverend Deacon Michael Malone_

6. Should we leave the house by 6_ o'clock if the party begins at 6_30?

7. My mother is reading *The Coloured Lands* by G.K. Chesterton _ which was not originally published until after his death.

8. When she was five, May Morris had one goal in life_ to learn to read.

Review of Semicolons and Colons

Indicate why the semicolon or colon was used in each sentence. Use the Reasons Bank on the next page.

Example: The sun was high, hot, and bright; everyone slathered on sunscreen.

joining independent clauses

1. We celebrated Easter with our grandparents on April 16, 2006; April 8, 2007; March 23, 2008; and April 12, 2009.

   _____

2. One of E.C. Bentley's first clerihews was highly scientific in nature:

   Sir Humphrey Davy
   Abominated gravy.
   He lived in the odium
   Of having discovered sodium.

   _____

3. Brave men are all vertebrates; they have their softness on the surface and their toughness in the middle. —G.K. Chesterton

   _____

4. There are only two ways of governing: by a rule and by a ruler. —G.K. Chesterton

   _____

5. When *Onions in My Boots: Basic Gardening for Young Sprouts* arrived in the mail, Thomas, Terri, Tammy, Theo, and Talia predicted that they would be growing vegetables.

   _____

6. The St. Scholastica Homeschool Co-op's Bible class begins at 8:15 a.m. every Wednesday.

   _____

7. Carlos pulled all his books out of his book bag: *The Happy Prince and Other Stories*, *Old Mother West Wind*, and *Aesop's Fables*.

   _____

8. Aldina's favorite Bible verse is Luke 9:48.

   _____

Reasons Bank

Joining independent clauses

Separating elements in a list

Distinguishing chapters and verses

Distinguishing hours and minutes

Distinguishing main title from subtitle

Separating a list from an independent clause

Separating a quotation and an independent clause

Separating an appositive at the end of an independent clause

Quotation Marks

We punctuate speech with quotation marks. This enables us to distinguish conversation, or dialogue, from the descriptive or narrative part of a story or essay. It also protects us from plagiarism, which is the theft of the thought. When we use someone else's original sentences word for word and do not give that writer credit, then we are committing a theft; we are plagiarizing.

Examples:

"Freedom consists not in doing what we like, but in having the right to do what we ought," said Pope John Paul II.

Notice that the comma goes inside the quotation marks when the name of the speaker ends the sentence.

Pope John Paul II said, "Freedom consists not in doing what we like, but in having the right to do what we ought."

Notice that the comma is placed immediately after "said" and is outside the quotation marks.

"Freedom consists not in doing what we like," said Pope John Paul II, "but in having the right to do what we ought."

Notice the placement of the commas, the quotation marks, and that the second half of the sentence is not capitalized when the quotation is interrupted.

Pope John Paul II defined freedom as "having the right to do what we ought."

Notice that no comma and no capital letter are used in this partial quotation.

READING QUOTATION MARKS EXERCISE

Read the commas and quotation marks aloud.

Example: Open quote "An excuse is worse and more terrible than a lie, comma for an excuse is a lie guarded, comma" close quote announced Pope John Paul II.

1. The essayist quoted Pope John XXIII, "Men are like wine—some turn to vinegar, but the best improve with age."

2. "Anger is as a stone cast into a wasp's nest," said Pope Paul VI.

3. "The external deserts in the world are growing," stated Pope Benedict XIV, "because the internal deserts have become so vast."

4. Pope Leo XIII understood the basic principle of capitalism when he remarked that "capital cannot do without labor, nor labor without capital."

5. Pope John Paul II knew that reason and faith could work together: "Science can purify religion from error and superstition. Religion can purify science from idolatry and false absolutes."

Even poets use quotation marks:

Sir Christopher Wren
Said, "I am going to dine with some men.
If anyone calls
Say I am designing St. Paul's."

—E.C. Bentley

Quotation Marks or Italics?

Use italics for complete works or major works. If you are handwriting a paper, a <u>wavy underline</u> represents italics. Use quotation marks for short works or parts of a larger work.

Examples:

"Adieu, warm sunshine" is sung at the end of Act I of Beethoven's opera *Fidelio*.

My favorite story from *The Happy Prince and Other Stories* is "The Selfish Giant."

We watched "Talking in Rhyme," an episode in the television series *G. K. Chesterton: Apostle of Common Sense*.

He memorized "Citizen of the World," a poem written by Joyce Kilmer.

The essay "Here is New York" gives E.B. White's impressions of his beloved city.

The Bible and Bible chapters are not italicized or placed in quotations.

Italics

plays, movies

long musical pieces

television and radio programs

artworks

famous speeches

long poems

books

web sites, magazines

names of vehicles

Quotation Marks

scenes or songs from plays and movies

shorter pieces within longer musical pieces

individual episodes

individual items in a larger display; photographs

sections of a speech or titles of speeches

short poems

titles of chapters, stories, short stories, essays

titles of magazine articles, web site articles

QUOTATION MARKS OR ITALICS EXERCISE

Decide whether the sentences below need quotation marks or italics. Some may need both. Add the quotation marks as required or draw a wavy underline for italics.

Example: Auguste Rodin's statue The Thinker was intended to represent Dante, the great poet.

1. I enjoyed reading the article Love and Loyalty in Gilbert Magazine.

2. The space shuttle Challenger is a marvel of modern engineering.

3. You need time to read the epic poem Beowulf.

4. Afghan Girl was taken in 1984 by photographer Steve McCurry for the National Geographic.

5. Her reading assignment was the chapter titled The Council of Elrond from The Lord of the Rings.

6. The radio program Catholic Answers Live featured the episode Miracle on the Hudson with Fred Beretta.

7. You can find the quotation in the Bible in Psalm 22.

8. Martin Luther King's speech I Have a Dream is often quoted.

9. They sang Silent Night in the car during the long road trip when they saw the first star appear.

10. The web site Catholic Culture contains a liturgical calendar, a blog, news, and reviews of other Catholic sites.

11. Valerie had a difficult time thinking of a title, but she finally called her story Teaching My Dog to Roll Over.

Apostrophes

You may think of the apostrophe as a high and mighty comma. It is a flag waving at you, saying, "You have left a letter, letters, or even words out, but fear not. I am strong enough to help you understand."

Apostrophes show possession:

Tess's three-story mansion, or the three-story mansion *belonging to* Tess

The lady's elegant red and black hat, or the elegant red and black hat *that belonged to the lady*

The children's sidewalk chalk, or the sidewalk chalk *that was given to the children*

The words in italics are the words that are left out when an apostrophe is used. These words are understood.

READING APOSTROPHES EXERCISE

Read these sentences aloud, saying "apostrophe s" at the appropriate points.

Example: Danielle's (apostrophe s) and Cass's (apostrophe s) horses are in the stable.

Bess's candle was lit.

The Evanses' candles were lit.

The men's candles were lit.

The children held each other's hands.

Everyone's candle was brightly glowing inside the darkened church.

Adding Apostrophes Exercise

Write in an apostrophe when the sentences require one.

Example: Milan's home was a perfect spot for a picnic because it had a beautiful lake filled with Ross's Geese.

1. Everyone appreciated the cooks skill when her delicious sandwiches appeared on the picnic tables.

2. Milans grandmother said the Lords Prayer, and then everybody sat down.

3. The boys spoons were balanced precariously on the ends of their noses.

4. Mr. Denniss applause in recognition of the boys balancing skills startled the geese.

5. The geeses reaction was to flap their wings, which caused the ladies hats to become airborne.

6. The ladies shrieks of dismay made everyone jump.

7. One hat struck Chriss spoon, and the spoon fell into Pauls lap.

8. The Camposes laughter over the incident was contagious, and soon everybodys sides were shaking.

Apostrophes and Ownership

Sometimes items can be owned jointly by people, such as a car or a house. Your toothbrush is not owned jointly. The placement of an apostrophe tells the reader about the ownership of items.

Mike and Thomas's horse is running through the field. (One horse is owned by both Mike and Thomas.)

Mrs. Hastings's books are on display. (Books written or owned by Mrs. Hastings.)

Notice that the verb refers to the number of the items not to the number of the owners. The horse is running. The books are on display.

Cal's and Cecily's mittens are on the shelf. (Cal and Cecily both own their own pair of mittens. Therefore both names receive the apostrophe s.)

OWNERSHIP EXERCISE

Determine if the ownership is joint or individual. Punctuate the sentences correctly with apostrophes and the letter s.

Examples: Sr. Mary's and Sr. Anne's prayer books are missing. (Each sister has her own individual prayer book, and so each name needs an apostrophe s.)

Sr. Mary and Sr. Anne's convent is located in San Antonio. (The sisters belong to the same convent, and so only one apostrophe s is used after the last name.)

1. Frances and Francis award-winning song "Celebrating Lifes Mysteries," which turned them into celebrities, also made them too nervous to go out in public.

2. Dave and Mitzi shoes were still muddy from their long trek home.

3. A cat and a dog noses were cold and damp.

4. Alexis and Nicholas car was crushed by a falling tree, which they discovered after returning from vacation.

5. The Smiths dog chased the squirrels in the park.

6. Patricia and Donald toothbrushes were packed in their suitcases.

7. Karl, Timothy, and Paula dogs are in the dog show.

Not all possessives require an apostrophe, as in "Its sharp teeth ripped apart his homework in minutes." Here we have two possessives, "its" and "his." Neither possessive needs an apostrophe. Why? Because we do not add apostrophes to possessive personal pronouns. Indefinite pronouns will use an apostrophe s, as in _Someone's umbrella was left out._

MECHANICS

Possession Without Apostrophe Exercise

Read these sentences aloud and do not add apostrophes. The possessive pronouns and possessive adjectives are underlined.

<u>My</u> books are overdue at the library. <u>Mine</u> are in <u>my</u> book bag.

<u>Yours</u> are also overdue.

<u>Hers</u> are not overdue.

<u>His</u> are awfully overdue. He will have to pay a huge fine.

<u>Its</u> intellect is not high enough for it to be allowed to check out books. Besides, only service dogs are allowed in the library.

<u>Whose</u> books are those?

<u>Theirs</u>. They will pick <u>their</u> books up in a minute.

Possessive Pronoun Exercise

Write ✓ if the pronouns are punctuated correctly. Make the correction if the sentence is not punctuated correctly.

Examples: _His_ His's shoes are over there.

_✓_ Nobody's hat has been hung up.

1. _____ We picked up somebody's coat and put it in the lost and found box.

2. _____ Ours are blue and white, and theirs are green and white.

3. _____ Who's rosary is that over there?

4. _____ The squirrel has an acorn in it's paws.

5. _____ They have an essay that appears to be yours judging by the italic handwriting that you often use.

6. _____ The hailstorm had damaged everyone's car.

7. _____ We borrowed one anothers pens.

8. _____ If its wings act as flippers and it lives in Antarctica, it must be a penguin.

Apostrophes and Contractions

postrophes also indicate contractions:

I'll means I will
'tis means It is
goin' means going
it's means it is or it has
who's means who is or who has
can't means can not

As you can see from these lines in James Whitcomb Riley's poem, "Little Orphant Annie," contractions are helpful when you want to leave letters out. Riley was known for writing in dialect, mimicking the actual sounds people made when they spoke.

Wunst they wuz a little boy wouldn't say his prayers,

An' when he went to bed at night, away up-stairs,

His Mammy heerd him holler, an' his Daddy heerd him bawl,

An' when they turn't the kivvers down, he wuzn't there at all!

An' they seeked him in the rafter-room, an' cubby-hole, an' press,

An' seeked him up the chimbly-flue, an' ever'-wheres, I guess;

But all they ever found wuz thist his pants an' roundabout:

An' the Gobble-uns 'll git you

Ef you

Don't

Watch

Out!

MECHANICS

CONTRACTIONS EXERCISE

Rewrite the sentences adding apostrophes only when required.

Example: His are the blue ones, and Sally didnt bring hers.

Correction: His are the blue ones, and Sally didn't bring hers.

1. Im going to meet you at your house as soon as youre ready.

   _____

2. Whos supposed to be at the birthday party?

   _____

3. We rented a video of *Singin in the Rain.*

   _____

4. Its got big, sharp teeth!

   _____

5. Whose big red pickup truck is parked in his yard?

   _____

6. Its bark was nearly as bad as its bite.

   _____

7. Their giggles couldnt be heard over the booming of the thunder.

   _____

8. Twas a brilliant plan, but it would never have worked.

   _____

Review of Quotation Marks, Italics, and Apostrophes

Write ✓ if the entire sentence is punctuated correctly.

Examples: _____ He said I'm not reading The Hobbit.

This sentence is not punctuated correctly because it is missing quotation marks and italics.

___✓___ He said, "I'm not reading *The Hobbit*."

1. _____ Who's going to Frank and Kelly's anniversary party?

2. _____ Whose going to Frank's and Kelly's anniversary party?

3. _____ Id like to read John Banister Tabb's poem *Jack Frosts Apology*.

4. _____ I'd like to read John Banister Tabb's poem "Jack Frost's Apology."

5. _____ "Watch out, they shouted because the wind is getting stronger and stronger!"

6. _____ "Watch out," they shouted, "because the wind is getting stronger and stronger!"

7. _____ Thats going to be a great book, isn't it? she said.

8. _____ "That's going to be a great book, isn't it?" she said.

9. _____ Terri's Aunt's Hannah's cats's names are Johann and Frederick.

10. _____ Terri's Aunt Hannah's cats' names are Johann and Frederick.

11. _____ We like to sing the song "My Favorite Things" from the musical *The Sound of Music*.

12. _____ We like to sing the song *My Favorite Things* from the musical "The Sound of Music."

Hyphens

We have already used hyphens to form some compound nouns, such as *sister-in-law* and *passer-by*. Hyphens are also used for compound adjectives.

Compound Adjectives:

Her two-week vacation to Italy was a graduation gift.

The blue-green gemstone was large.

That car has four-wheel drive.

Notice that the hyphenated compound adjective is placed before the **noun** in each sentence above. If the compound adjective does not precede the noun, the hyphens are usually but not always dropped. Use a dictionary for assistance if you are not sure.

Example: The well-bred horse may win the race. That horse is well bred and may win the race.

Compound verbs are usually not hyphenated but written as one word, as *overarching* and *underperforming*, and *upgrading*.

Also hyphenate all spelled-out numbers from twenty-one to ninety-nine and all fractions.

Examples: thirty-one soldiers

one-third of the soldiers

but one hundred two soldiers, or 102 soldiers, never one-hundred-two

HYPHENATING COMPOUND ADJECTIVES EXERCISE

Add hyphens to the adjectives, numbers, and fractions as required. Use a dictionary if necessary.

Examples: The friendly looking cat jumped on the sofa.
Correction: The friendly–looking cat jumped on the sofa.

The cat, which was friendly looking, jumped on the sofa.
No correction as the compound adjective does not precede the noun.

MECHANICS

1. That family is *well liked* by *nine tenths* of the people in the town.

2. A *heat seeking* camera can show images on the darkest nights.

3. The new satellite, which has been *long anticipated* by *forty three* scientists, will be sent to another solar system.

4. The *one hundred solar powered* rockets didn't go very high.

5. Her *ten minute* phone call lasted half an hour.

6. *Sixty six* dollars was the cost of the repairs.

7. Give her the *left handed* scissors.

8. Mrs. Bailey is *kind hearted*.

9. The *broken hearted* girl sobbed into her pillow.

10. An *eight sided* figure is an octagon.

More Uses for Hyphens

Use hyphens with the prefixes self-, ex-, and all-.

Examples:

They felt self-conscious.

The ex-Marine was wounded.

God is All-Powerful.

Use a hyphen with prefixes to avoid confusion or when the word following a prefix begins with the same letter the prefix ends with.

Examples:

The citizens felt repressed. (The citizens felt intimidated.)
The pants had to be re-pressed. (The pants had to be ironed again.)

Pre-existing condition is preferable to preexisting condition.
The homeschooler's co-op, not the homeschooler's coop.

Use a hyphen between prefixes and capitalized words and between prefixes and numbers or letters.

Examples:

un-American

mid-1900s

pre-Vatican II

READING HYPHENS EXERCISE

Read these sentences, including the hyphens, aloud.

Example: In mid-hyphen March, our co-hyphen op prepared twenty-hyphen four green hats for St. Patrick's Day.

1. Self-assured, we ventured down the one-way street wearing our rose-colored glasses.

2. They were semi-independent because at the age of twenty-two, the twins owned two-thirds of a small business.

3. The ex-football player was rescued in mid-December.

4. In the mid-1990s, our dry-cleaning bills were sky high, usually costing about forty-five dollars a week.

5. We should re-sign the pro-life petition since the paper got wet, and our original signatures smeared.

6. The long-legged spider was crawling up the rough-hewn wall.

7. G. K. Chesterton has been falsely accused of anti-Semitism, which is strange because he was one of the first to speak out against Hitler's evil-minded treatment of the Jews.

To Hyphenate or Not Exercise

Use a dictionary if necessary to determine whether or not to add hyphens to the following italicized words.

Example: He was *self educated.*

Correction: He was *self–educated.*

1. The Smithsonian Institution is a *quasi official* federal agency.

2. The *fast paced* race was soon over.

3. The cake was only *half baked.*

4. The *half note* is not held as long as a *whole note.*

5. Her *long range* plan was to visit South America.

6. She was *forty odd* years old.

7. All the children sat *cross legged.*

8. The *Franco Prussian* War was a conflict between France and Prussia.

9. *Cross talk* refers to interference between radio channels.

10. The students showed great *self restraint* although they were falsely accused.

Dashes

Use a dash to announce a sudden break or interruption or to signal your reader that a long appositive, definition, or summary is next. A dash is also used to give credit to an author after a quotation. A dash is less formal than both a colon and parentheses, and it is often used to **emphasize** the interruption.

Examples:

Supercilious—coolly and patronizingly haughty

Mrs. Thomas wanted to finish the long novel—yes, it was eight hundred pages of text with no illustrations of any kind—before sunrise.

If the old man wanted to plant oak trees all day instead of sitting in front of the television—who were we to try to stop him?

"I believe in getting into hot water; it keeps you clean." —G. K. Chesterton

INFORMAL DASH EXERCISE

Rewrite the sentences on a separate sheet of paper, replacing the formal punctuation with the informal dash.

Example: If I land in the castle moat when I try my new flying machine . . . well, what will the alligators think?

Informal revision: <u>If I land in the castle moat when I try my new flying machine—</u>
<u>well, what will the alligators think?</u>

1. The day was sunny and bright (not a day on which you would expect the storm clouds of disaster to rain down upon you), and the birds were sweetly trilling on the lamp posts.

2. Whatever the children may have thought of asparagus soup, and they had often thought of feeding it to the dog, it was greatly appreciated by the adults.

3. "And you are implying . . .?"
   "That we will be late if you don't hurry."

4. time: the measured or measurable period during which an action, process, or condition exists or continues

5. That crazy mockingbird sat in the oak tree and belted out its songs: the tone of a cell phone, whistling, the cackle of a grackle, whining, and the roar of a lawn mower.

6. Musicians from around the globe (Hungary, Egypt, Ireland, Taiwan, Canada, and Honduras) enjoyed the international computer music conference.

7. I know that I have seen your face many times before, but I can't remember . . .

Emily Dickinson used dashes frequently in her verses. Early editors changed her punctuation, but later her use of dashes was restored. The dashes make her poetry appear breathless, spontaneous, and unfinished as the short poem below illustrates. Until you become a world-famous author, restrain your use of the dash.

What I can do — I will —
Though it be little as a Daffodil —
That I cannot — must be
Unknown to possibility —

MECHANICS

Photocopying of these pages is a violation of copyright law.

151

Parentheses

Parentheses are more formal than the dash. We enclose an interruption or explanation with parentheses to avoid overemphasizing the interruption or explanation. We use parentheses to set off dates, citations, numbers, and numerical or alphabetical lists.

Examples of Interruption and Explanation:

She was happy (far happier than we had ever seen her before) when we switched her dog food.

Judging by his bookshelves, Mr. Hawkins is quite the antiquarian (a person who collects rare and ancient books).

We admired the elegant silver Duesenberg. (It had been owned by someone in Europe with an aristocratic title.) The car had been purchased by a museum in the U.S. and restored after careful research.

Examples with Numbers:

The amount due is one hundred one dollars ($101).

J. R. R. Tolkien (1892-1973) was a professor at Oxford.

The ideal candidate for this office should exhibit (1) attention to detail, (2) a good sense of humor, (3) honesty, and (4) goodwill to all.

Adding numbers enclosed in parentheses is **not** always appropriate:
She is five years old (5). *Correction:* She is five years old.

USING PARENTHESES EXERCISE

Add parentheses if the underlined phrase needs enclosing. Not every sentence will require a parenthesis.

Example: St. Jean Vianney <u>commonly known as the Curé d'Ars</u> is the patron saint of parish priests.

Revision: St. Jean Vianney (commonly known as the Curé d'Ars) is the patron saint of parish priests.

1. Jean Baptiste Marie Vianney <u>1786-1859</u> was born on a farm in France.

2. Although young Jean was studying to become a priest, he was conscripted <u>compelled to join the military</u> because Napoleon needed new recruits.

3. Jean's regiment left without him because he went to the church to pray before the departure, <u>but the captain of the barracks sent him to find the regiment</u> instead of arresting him.

4. Jean wound up in Noes with a group of deserters <u>his father was not happy when he discovered this situation some months later</u>, and the mayor of Noes persuaded Jean to remain in the town to teach.

5. Eventually, Jean passed the necessary examination to enter the seminary <u>he struggled with Latin and failed the first examination.</u>

6. As the Curé of Ars, Jean Vianney gave advice and consolation to <u>1</u> bishops, <u>2</u> priests, <u>3</u> religious brothers and sisters, <u>4</u> those in doubt about their vocation, and <u>5</u> great and small sinners from all over France and beyond.

7. Pope Pius XI canonized the Curé of Ars in 1925, <u>sixty-six years</u> after the priest's death.

Citations of Works

Parentheses are also used to cite works when giving credit to an author and to locate lines in plays or poetry.

Example of a Citation of a Poem:

In *Lepanto*, Chesterton frequently uses alliteration, as in "Dim drums throbbing, in the hills half heard" (line 15).

Example of a Citation of a Play:

Proceed, Solinus, to procure my fall,
And by the doom of death end woes and all. (*Comedy of Errors*, I.i.1-2)

The title of the play is given unless the work is referring to only one play. The number of the act is indicated in capital Roman numerals, the number of the scene in miniscule Roman numerals, and the corresponding lines in ordinary numerals.

Examples of a Citation to a Page or Pages:

You have already been introduced to the equation for determining the surface area of a sphere (p. 205).

The implications of Shakespeare's father's spiritual will are not to be overlooked (Pearce, pp. 30-38).

The abbreviation *p.* refers to one page while *pp.* refers to more than one page.

Parentheses in Citations Exercise

Add parentheses as necessary.

1. In *The Comedy of Errors*, Adriana meets the Abbess who reprimands her for her behavior toward her husband. V.i.68-89

2. Reviewing the paragraphs on fungi p. 119 will help you prepare for the exam.

3. Too proud, too proud, what a press she bore!
   Royal, and all her royals wore.
   Sharp with her, shorten sail!
   Too late; lost; gone with the gale. *Loss of the Eurydice*, lines 33-36

4. Some modern critics do not care for Chesterton's assertion that Shakespeare was Catholic, but this "state of modern literary criticism" betrays a serious lack of understanding about how beliefs inspire writers Pearce, p. 174 .

5. The discussion of imaginary numbers pp. 315-320 is poorly written.

6. Writers are warned against constructing awkward adverbs like "tangledly" Strunk and White, pp. 75-76 .

Abbreviations

We use abbreviations to shorten words. Imagine having to write out "Mister Juan Pablo Seguin, Certified Public Accountant, will arrive at two post meridiem." Without worrying about being misunderstood, we could write "Mr. Juan Pablo Seguin, CPA, will arrive at 2:00 p.m."

We abbreviate titles:

Mr. — Mister

Mrs. — Mistress but pronounced "missus" or "missis"

Dr. — Doctor

Rep. — Representative

Sen. — Senator

St. — Saint

Fr. — Father, for a priest

Sr. — Sister, referring to a religious sister

Jr. — Junior

Sr. — Senior

M.D. — Medical Doctor

Ph.D. — Doctor of Philosophy

Miss and Ms. are not abbreviations, although they are titles. Miss is used to refer to unmarried women and Ms. is used when the writer is not sure of the marital status of the female being addressed.

There are many more titles that are abbreviated. Use a dictionary if you need clarification of what the abbreviation stands for.

Countries, states, companies, famous people and ordinary objects are also commonly abbreviated.

Examples:

U.S. or USA, LI, VA — United States, Liechtenstein, Vatican City

CA, NY, CO — California, New York, Colorado

IBM, CNN — International Business Machines, Cable News Network

JFK, MLK — John F. Kennedy, Martin Luther King

DVD, RAM — digital video disc, random-access memory

Numbers are often used with abbreviations.

A.D. 1998 — anno domini, in the year of the Lord

1998 B.C. — 1,998 years before the birth of Christ

25 mph — twenty-five miles per hour, do not use periods

25 mpg — twenty-five miles per gallon, do not use periods

1 p.m. — one o'clock in the afternoon, post meridiem (after midday)

1 a.m. — one hour after midnight, ante meridiem (before midday)

125 in. — 125 inches, use a period to avoid confusion with the preposition "in"

125 cm — 125 centimeters, no period

125 lb — 125 pounds

125 mm — 125 millimeters

125 tsp — 125 teaspoons, not to be confused with Tbsp., which means tablespoons

ABBREVIATIONS EXERCISE

At least one word in each sentence may be abbreviated. Write the correct abbreviations in the blanks.

Example: Miss Kyra Caulkins was born in the year of the Lord 1901. _A.D._

1. The headquarters of Eternal Word Television Network are in Irondale, Alabama. _____

2. Doctor Melissa Brainerd is a neurosurgeon. _____

3. Type the Uniform Resource Locator into the browser window. _____

4. That coin can't possibly be stamped with the date 2001 Before Christ. _____

5. At 2:30 post meridiem, we will begin the party. _____

6. Is that phone call for Robert Lawson, Senior, or Robert Lawson, Junior? _____

    _____

7. The digital video recorders are now on sale. _____

8. If the coti-cara can travel as fast as .022 miles per hour, how long will it take the coti-cara to get

    from First Street to Second Street? _____

9. We were looking everywhere for Father Brown and Sister Josepha. _____ _____

10. Which version of the Bible is that—the King James Version, the New American Bible, or the

    Revised Standard Version? _____ _____ _____

Understanding Abbreviations Exercise

Write out the complete word or phrase for each abbreviation. You may need to use a dictionary.

Example: PDF ___*portable document format*___

1. EU (a group of countries) _____

2. AAA _____

3. B.A. _____

4. BBQ _____

5. CIA _____

6. DJ _____

7. DNA _____

8. GB (either a country or a term used in digital information storage)

_____

9. F (referring to temperature) _____

10. IRS _____

11. Msgr. _____

12. S (direction) _____

13. R.N. _____

14. ppm (used to measure relative proportions) _____

Latin Abbreviations

You may see Latin abbreviations in some academic works although these abbreviations are used less and less frequently.

Here are some common Latin abbreviations and their meanings:

AMDG	Ad maiorem Dei gloriam	for the greater glory of God
c. ca	circa	about, approximately
DG	Dei Gratia	by the grace of God
e.g.	exempli gratia	for example, for instance
et al.	et allii, et alia	and other people/things
etc.	et cetera	and so on, and other things
ib, ibid.	ibidem	in the same place/author (esp. previous reference)
i.e.	id est	that is to say (in other words); do not use this abbreviation in place of e.g.
lb	libra	scales, used to refer to weight in pounds
ms.	manuscriptum	a manuscript, written by hand; or simply a document
N.B.	nota bene	note well, pay attention
op. cit.	opere citato	in the work cited/mentioned before
P.S.	post scriptum	after what has been written
Re:	in re	concerning, in the matter of (used in memos)
R.I.P.	requiescat in pace	may he or she rest in peace
s.o.s.	si opus sit	if there is need, if necessary
v., vs.	versus	against
v.v.	vice versa	the other way round

LATIN ABBREVIATIONS EXERCISE

Write the English meaning of the Latin abbreviation or the Latin abbreviation for the English meaning in the blanks provided.

Example: lb _pounds_

1. vs. _____

2. N.B. _____

3. that is to say, namely _____

4. may he/she rest in peace _____

5. for the greater glory of God _____

6. concerning, in the matter of _____

7. e. g. _____

8. op. cit. _____

9. and other people/things _____

10. P.S. _____

11. the other way round _____

12. ibid. _____

13. DG _____

14. and so on _____

The Ampersand &

The ampersand is not technically an abbreviation, but it is commonly used. The symbol is derived from the combination of the letters e and t. The word "et" is Latin for "and." So when you see the ampersand (&), read it as the word "and." Do not use it in formal writing unless you are quoting or the ampersand is used as part of the name of a business or title, as in *Town & Country Magazine.*

Chapman & Hall
Swore not at all.
Mr. Chapman's yea was yea,
And Mr. Hall's nay was nay. — E. C. Bentley

Writing Numbers

To make reading numbers as simple as possible, grammar has rules about when to spell out numbers.

Spell out single-digit numbers and simple fractions.

Examples:

We now have *zero* ballpoint pens in the house, but yesterday we had *nine*.
Please take *one-half* the cookies and *one-third* of the cake.

Remember to hyphenate spelled out fractions and numbers between twenty-one and ninety-nine.

But write complex fractions as numbers:

We need 5 $\frac{1}{2}$ gallons of paint.

Spell out numbers that begin sentences, or revise the sentence so the number does not appear first.

Examples:

Thirty-two Duesenbergs are on display. The display contains 32 Duesenbergs.

Be consistent:

I would like two cats and twelve dogs. I would like 2 cats and 12 dogs.

Be clear:

I want twelve 20-ounce cans of beans. (I will never want 12 20-ounce cans of beans, nor will I ever want twelve twenty-ounce cans of beans. Switch between written words and numbers to avoid confusion. Usually, you will spell out the smaller number.)

Write large numbers as simply as possible.

Examples:

I have answered over one million math questions.
I have answered 1, 002, 119 math questions.
I would like 511 sprinkles on this ice cream cone.
I would like only two hundred sprinkles on this cone.

WRITING NUMBERS EXERCISE

Write C if the numbers are correctly written. Otherwise, correct the numbers by spelling them out or by writing the figures.

Example: _____ He paid for 12 apples and two oranges. *Or* He paid for 12 apples and two oranges.

(handwritten above "12": 2) *(handwritten above "two": twelve)*

1. _____ 49 of the homeschoolers were preparing to travel to Italy.

2. _____ The mother ordered two 20-foot lengths of rope for the science experiment.

3. _____ Mr. and Mrs. Ricardi had 0 interest in learning to skydive.

4. _____ Because we averaged our grades incorrectly, we ended up with a score of nine hundred fifty-one instead of 93.

5. _____ We saved $^1/_3$ of the pizza for breakfast the following morning because we like cold pizza first thing in the morning.

6. _____ Should you buy 11 $^1/_4$ yards of velvet for the curtains?

7. _____ The large box contained seven thousand buttons.

8. _____ The small box contained 10,000,000 paper clips.

It's About Time

When using the contraction **o'clock**, spell out numbers, as in **nine o'clock**. When using the abbreviations **a.m.** and **p.m.**, write the numeral, as in **11: 30 p.m.** To avoid confusion, write 12:00 **midnight** or 12:00 **noon**, instead of a.m. and p.m. These are okay:

I'm leaving at one-thirty.
I'm leaving at 1:30.
I'm leaving at 1:30 p.m.
I'm leaving at 1:30 this afternoon.
I'm leaving at one-thirty this afternoon.
2001 was an eventful year. But try to reword it: The year 2001 was eventful.

But not these:

I'm leaving at one-thirty o'clock.
1:30 is when I'm leaving.

Write out terms such as half-past, a quarter till, and a quarter past. Hyphenate "half-past." Racing Times are exact with hours, minutes, and seconds in that order.

In 2009, Mikitenko won the London Marathon in 2:22:11.

TIME EXERCISE

Write the correct form of time in each blank.

Example: _Five o'clock_ is when I arrive in Buzzard's Roost, Mississippi. (2:00 p.m.,

Five o'clock, twelve-thirty o'clock)

1. The blue team showed up at _____ . (8:45 p.m., 12:00 a.m., 6 midnight)

2. The bus left at _____ . (one fifty p.m., 12:00 noon, seven-o-one p.m.)

3. At _____ , we will turn on the television to listen to Dale Ahlquist expound

   on the philosophy and writing of G. K. Chesterton. (9:00 p.m., nine o'clock, nine in the evening)

4. _____ is much too late to be getting to bed. (3:30 a.m., Three-thirty in the

   morning, three thirty)

5. Although she did not win the marathon, her time was respectable at _____ .

   (3: 30: 49, three hours, thirty seconds, and forty-nine minutes, over three hours)

6. We left at _____ ten and returned at seven in the evening. (1/2 after, half-

   past, 0:30 minutes)

7. If the minute hand of a clock is pointing to the number 3, then it must be a

   _____ the hour. (half-past, quarter-after, quarter after)

Review of Dashes and Parentheses

Write C if the sentence is punctuated correctly. If the italicized word or phrases is not punctuated correctly, write "dash" or "parenthesis" if either of these marks would be correct.

Example: <u>parenthesis</u> Socrates *born around 469 B.C.* is a well-known Greek philosopher who did not write philosophy texts.

1. _____ We know about Socrates *(Σωκράτης, in the Greek alphabet)* from the writings of Plato.

2. _____ "The hour of departure has arrived, and we go our ways—I to die and you to live. Which is the better, only God knows." *Socrates*

3. _____ We learned about *1. electrons, 2. protons, and 3. neutrons.*

4. _____ I'm leaving this instant *after I put away my books, answer the telephone, and feed the dog.*

5. _____ FAQ—*Frequently Asked Question*

6. _____ The MacKenzie family enjoyed Shakespeare—*why else would they have named their pets Romeo, Hamlet, and Beatrice?*

7. _____ The Latin exercises on the subjunctive *(pp. 78-81)* are due today.

8. _____ Now Beowulf bode in the burg of the Scyldings,
leader beloved, and long he ruled—*lines 1-2.*

9. _____ Socrates *the horse, not the philosopher* enjoyed rolling in the grass.

10. _____ According to proper etiquette in the late 1800s, when visiting, you must "be perfectly certain that your visit will be agreeable" *Hill, p. 162.*

Review of Abbreviations and Numbers

Choose the best word, abbreviation, or number for each sentence.

Example: The circus will begin at ___*six-thirty*___ in the evening. (six-thirty, six thirty, 6- thirty)

1. At 5:30 _____ , we got in the car for our long car trip. (B.C., a.m., am)

2. _____ provides wireless, DSL, telephone, and television service. (BMW, DJIA, AT&T)

3. _____ of the homeschoolers are going on the field trip to the train museum. ($^2/_3$, two thirds, Two-thirds)

4. We used _____ 5-lb bags of flour to make all the pizzas for our party. (2, two, 2:00)

5. Then we opened twelve _____ -ounce bags of cheese to sprinkle on top. (16, six-teen, sixteen)

6. If this car gets 100 _____ , then we should think about buying it. (miles per gallon, MPG, mpg)

7. 1 ft = 12 _____ (inches, in, in.)

8. Our public library contains _____ books. (5,117; five thousand one hundred seventeen; five-thousand one-hundred seventeen)

9. Are we supposed to read pages _____ ? (1-5; one through five; 1 through five)

10. How do you like to celebrate _____ Patrick's Day? (ST, St., Saint)

11. We have _____ oaks, 12 crape myrtles, and 13 pecan trees. (nine, 9, 09)

12. At 12 _____ , the fireworks show will end. (p.m., a.m., midnight)

Edmund Clerihew Bentley (1875-1956), a British editor, writer and humorist, who is best known for *Trent's Last Case*, a classic detective story. Bentley and Chesterton went to the same school, St. Paul's, and were close friends throughout their lives. Bentley invented the clerihew, a nonsensical biographical poem of four lines. In turn, others have clerihewed Bentley:

When studying too intently,
Refresh yourself with Bentley.
You could do much worse
Than to read his light verse.

Composition

When you say something, make sure you have said it. The chances of your having said it are only fair. —*The Elements of Style* by William Strunk, Jr. and E. B. White

Attention

We build meaning with words, and our words come together into sentences, which are complete thoughts. Our sentences should flow one after the other in a logical, clear progression that aims at saying what we mean. Along the way, we need to hold our readers' attention.

Attention! If we do not consider our reader and make the journey through our writing pleasant, clear, or interesting, then we have lost our reader. Choosing lively words, using correct spelling and grammar (unless you are writing in dialect like James Whitcomb Riley), and varying sentence lengths and sentence structures are all elements that keep readers reading.

Lively Words

Pay attention to your nouns and verbs. Be precise. Use the right words consistently. An academic paper calls for one level of vocabulary and a casual conversation calls for another. Some words and phrases are formal, and some are informal and more relaxed.

WORD CHOICE EXERCISE

Write "Informal" if the selection uses casual, relaxed words. Write "Formal" if the selection uses authoritative, reserved words.

Examples:

<u>Formal</u>   "Take that banner down! 'tis tattered;/Broken is its shaft and shattered" — Fr. Abram Joseph Ryan

<u>Informal</u>   "O The Raggedy Man! He works fer Pa;/An' he's the goodest man ever you saw!" — James Whitcomb Riley

1. _____ "Do not attempt to use dialect unless you are a devoted student of the tongue you hope to reproduce. If you use dialect, be consistent." — *The Elements of Style*

2. _____ "The winds of wrath came driving him,/and blindly in the foam he fled/From west to east and errandless,/Unheralded he homeward sped." — J. R. R. Tolkien

3. _____ "Now quicker the fiddle went deedle-dum-diddle;/The dog began to roar,/The cow and the horses stood on their heads;/The guests all bounded from their beds/And danced upon the floor." — J. R. R. Tolkien

4. _____ "Deep, tender, firm and true, the Nation's heart/Throbs for her gallant heroes passed away,/Who in grim Battle's drama played their part,/And slumber here to-day" — James Whitcomb Riley

5. _____ "You better mind yer parunts, an' yer teachurs fond an' dear,/An' cherish them 'at loves you, an' dry the orphant's tear,/An' he'p the pore an' needy ones 'at clusters all about,/Er the Gobble-uns 'll git you/Ef you/Don't/Watch/Out!" — James Whitcomb Riley

6. _____ "It was a weakness of Voltaire's/To forget to say his prayers,/And one which to his shame/He never overcame." — E. C. Bentley

7. _____ "Before beginning to compose something, gauge the nature and extent of the enterprise and work from a suitable design. Design informs even the simplest structure, whether of brick and steel or of prose." —*The Elements of Style*

Clichés

Clichés are common and come easily to mind (*easy as pie*), but they drain your writing of liveliness. We do not want a succession of them in our writing because they tire our readers. (They do not *improve with age*, and they do not get your message across *loud and clear*.) The italicized phrases are all clichés.

FINDING CLICHÉS EXERCISE

To avoid clichés, you have to be able to find them. Underline clichés in the following sentences. Not every sentence will have a cliché.

Example: The sight of all that gold <u>made my eyes pop out of my head</u>.

1. You could buy that old house for a song.

2. Mr. Calhoun wanted to be a millionaire even though he knew that money can't buy happiness.

3. Those pancakes melted in my mouth.

4. After surviving and winning the Third Most Important Yacht Race of the Season and finding buried treasure and losing it again, Red Rowdy arrived home.

5. I'm sorry to burst your bubble, but you may not eat dessert first.

6. You may wear your sword as long as you abide by all the rules of parade etiquette and don't go swatting the parade watchers.

7. He knew he didn't have a leg to stand on when he was caught with his hand in the bag of chocolates.

Clichés may seem colorful because they do often use lively verbs. Beginning writers have a tendency to use easily accessible verbs. They sometimes use too many *to be* verbs, such as *am, is, are, was, were, being*, and *been*. Don't avoid using these verbs, but beware of overusing them.

COMPOSITION

The Sound of Being Exercise

Read these paragraphs aloud to listen to the sound of a paragraph filled with forms of the verb *to be* and a paragraph that has been revised. Underline all the *to be* verbs in both paragraphs.

My dog was a racing greyhound. His name was Hi Warlock, which is too fierce a name for his sweet disposition. He is now called Lock, which is not the best name for him, but it is better than Hi Warlock. We are happy to have adopted Lock because he is a great housedog now. He is quiet and obedient. He is our favorite dog.

In his previous life, our greyhound raced for a living. Greyhound owners give their racers fierce and memorable names to add to the thrill of racing. (While racing may thrill the fans, racing greyhounds suffer a miserable existence.) When we saw his name "Hi Warlock" written on his kennel at the adoption agency, we knew that must change. The adoption staff called him Lock. Because he was timid and frightened, we decided to continue calling him Lock although we sometimes call him Pinocchio because greyhounds have long noses.

To Be or Not To Be Exercise

Rewrite this paragraph, replacing most or all of the to be verbs with strong verbs. Answers will vary, but one possible solution is provided in the answer key.

Cooking is fun. Cooking in Epicuria is even more fun. Everyone in Epicuria is a cook. Some are bread bakers, some are pasta makers, some are expert at grilling, and many are fond of tossing salads. Everyone in Epicuria is fond of eating and of sharing food with friends.

Sentence Variety

Vary your sentences. A young child may be delighted with "See Spot. Run, Spot. Spot can run. Run faster, Spot." But unless your reader is a young child, you need to use a variety of sentence lengths that carry the reader and your meaning along.

While you don't want a long succession of short sentences, avoid never-ending sentences. You don't want sentences that all begin or end with dependent clauses. One appositive after another is too many appositives.

Let's look at the variety of sentences used by E. B. White:

> "My pigpen is at the bottom of an old orchard below the house. The pigs I have raised have lived in a faded building that once was an icehouse. There is a pleasant yard to move about in, shaded by an apple tree that overhangs the low rail fence. A pig couldn't ask for anything better—or none has, at any rate."

The first sentence is simple and short with a series of prepositions. The second sentence uses two restrictive clauses and is longer than the first sentence. The third sentence, being even longer than the second, contains a long dependent participial phrase. The last sentence consists of two brief thoughts tied together by an informal dash.

SENTENCE VARIETY EXERCISE

Describe the variety of sentences used in this paragraph by G. K. Chesterton. Use words that you have studied in this workbook, such as simple, compound, or complex sentence; parentheses, appositive. Answers will vary, but suggested answers are provided in the answer key.

But as I sat scrawling these silly figures on the brown paper, it began to dawn on me, to my great disgust, that I had left one chalk, and that a most exquisite and essential chalk, behind. I searched all my pockets, but I could not find any white chalk. Now, those who are acquainted with all the philosophy (nay, religion) which is typified in the art of drawing on brown paper, know that white is positive and essential. I cannot avoid remarking here upon a moral significance. One of the wise and awful truths which this brown-paper art reveals, is this, that white is a colour. It is not a mere absence of colour; it is a shining and affirmative thing, as fierce as red, as definite as black.

COMPOSITION

Writing Sentences Exercise

Look about you and find one thing to describe, using four sentences. On your own paper, write at least one simple sentence, one compound sentence and one complex sentence. Answers will vary.

Example: It's now an empty plastic container. Before I began writing, the container was not empty at all. I can't be expected to write without fuel to encourage the creative embers within, and so I had taken the precaution of filling the container with chocolate-covered peanuts yesterday. Alas, the peanuts have vanished.

Writing More Sentences Exercise

Think about your favorite activity and describe it in four sentences. On your own paper, use prepositions to describe where you perform this activity and use one appositive. Answers will vary.

Example: On the edge of the city on a heavily wooded hillside, I stride along the paved hiking trail. The paved trail, wide and level and appropriate for young children, will soon surrender to the steepness of the terrain. Soft mulch and then loose gravel and rocks will unwind before me through the juniper and scrub oaks. My legs will feel the burn of the labor required to reach the top of the limestone heap, and I will be tempted to stop and rest, but I won't.

The Effective Paragraph

Paragraphs may be any length from one sentence to several. Begin each paragraph with a sentence that indicates the topic or contains an explanation of the direction in which you are about to move, which is also known as a transition. Paragraphs are signs to the reader that a change is occurring. The writer has completed one topic and is moving on to another in an essay or a story or a newspaper report.

If you see this symbol ¶ on a written paper, it means you need to begin a new paragraph at that place.

A paragraph cannot be effective if you don't know what your topic is. Each paragraph should have one topic. So let's practice topics.

INDICATING THE TOPIC EXERCISE

Choose the best sentence to begin these paragraphs. Ask yourself what the topic is.

Choices:

Nursing homes are useful institutions. (Is the topic nursing homes?)

Barbara Walters should be more careful about her predictions because people aren't listening. (Is the topic Barbara Walters?)

There was a wedding in town this winter. (Is the topic weddings or marriage?)

Paragraph: Walter Crockett, our master carpenter and cabinet-maker, got married at the age of ninety-three. He met his bride—a younger woman—in the nursing home where they had both gone to die: and, such is the power of love, they sprang from the home and are happily settled in Penobscot, keeping house. This, it seems to me, pretty well takes the wind out of Barbara Walters' sails. I heard her say on television that marriage, as we know it, is on the way out and will be gone by the year 2000. — E. B. White

Choices:

We live in the anxiety of a fire breaking out and sweeping down upon us. (Is the paragraph about the fear of fire?)

No rain has fallen in several weeks. (Is the paragraph about dry weather?)

I'm not a trout fisherman, but my neighbors are. (Is the paragraph about fishing?)

Paragraph: The gardens are dry, the road to the shore is dusty. The ditches, which in May are usually swollen to bursting, are not more than a summer trickle. Trout fishermen are not allowed on the streams; pond fishing from a boat is still permissible. The landscape is lovely to behold, but the hot, dry wind carries the smell of trouble. The other day we saw the smoke of a fire over in the direction of the mountain.

Writing Topic Sentences Exercise

Write a short topic sentence to introduce the following topics. (Answers will vary.)

A skill I would like to learn this year:

_____

_____

What I predict is most likely to happen next week:

_____

_____

How my family is different from other families:

_____

_____

Why self-control is necessary:

_____

_____

Examples of Effective Paragraphs

What else makes a paragraph effective? Effective means "successful" or "capable of achieving the desired result, or effect." So writing an effective paragraph depends upon what result you desire. If you want to persuade your reader, then the effective paragraph will be persuasive with detailed proof of your point. If you want to describe a landscape, then you want to write a paragraph that allows the reader to see the shapes and colors and sounds that you do. If you desire to create suspense, then an effective paragraph will hint but not explain everything.

Let's look at some examples of effective paragraphs.

> "We have now reached the great break in the life of Francis of Assisi; the point at which something happened to him that must remain greatly dark to most of us, who are ordinary and selfish men whom God has not broken to make anew." —*Saint Francis of Assisi*, G. K. Chesterton

This paragraph is a short transitional paragraph. It explains to the reader what the author is going to try to illustrate but what may be difficult to understand. Chesterton warns the reader; he doesn't simply plunge into a complex interpretation.

> "The utterly unaltered voice and attitude added a strange violence to that shocking change of speech. But the guarder of the relic only seemed to turn his head by the smallest section of the compass. He seemed still to have a somewhat foolish face turned to the stars. Perhaps he had not understood. Or, perhaps, he had understood and sat rigid with terror." — "The Blue Cross," G. K. Chesterton

This paragraph from a fiction story describes the reaction of one character to another. A thief has revealed his intentions in the previous paragraph, and Chesterton moves to a new paragraph to indicate the effect of this revelation on the intended victim. The paragraph gives the reader an idea of the emotional atmosphere and of the unexpected reaction of the intended victim.

You do not want a succession of one sentence paragraphs unless you are writing a dialogue. In a dialogue, each speaker gets a new paragraph.

Example:
Mr. Malabar asked, "Who's got the secret code?"
"Me, sir," came the reply out of the dark.
"Who is me?" Mr. Malabar said.
"It's me, Melvin, sir," said Melvin.
"Okay, and where's Mervin?" asked Mr. Malabar.
"Right here, sir," was the reply.
Someone bumped Mr. Malabar's elbow. He assumed that the bumper was Mervin, but it was far too dark to see a face.

These paragraphs are effective because each new paragraph indicates a new speaker.

EFFECTIVE PARAGRAPHS EXERCISE

Read each pair of paragraphs below and check ✓ the one that is more effective.

1. _____ It was the funniest thing we ever saw!! The baby laughed and laughed. If the mom held up a cookie, the baby laughed. If the dad waved a toy, the baby laughed. We started laughing too. We couldn't help ourselves.

   _____ Tom invited me to his house, but he wouldn't tell me why. I thought we would go up to his room to build something with one of his construction sets. Instead we went to the den where his mom and dad were playing with his baby brother. When Tom's mom held up a cookie, the baby looked at it and giggled. Then his dad held up a rattle, and the baby laughed. Soon we were all laughing.

2. _____ E. B. White preferred to understate rather than overstate. He did not use spectacular words but relied on plain ones. He wrote about ordinary things that might seem boring, yet most things in life seemed to interest him—kitchens, storms, trains, dogs, pigs, and the volunteer fire department. White wasn't trying to impress his reader; he simply wanted to share his interest in life.

   _____ When he wrote, E. B. White used understatement often. Never use a ten-dollar word when a ten-center would do. Things didn't amaze him. But he wrote about a lot of different kinds of things. He was an intelligent man and a good writer. I enjoy reading his writing because he used understatement, which I think is a good way to write. Some day, maybe I can write as good as White did.

3. _____ Mother Angelica made up her mind to build a Catholic television network on the grounds of her monastery in Irondale, Alabama. Many people advised her to give up this expensive and highly technical undertaking. Yet in 1981, the Eternal Word Television Network (EWTN) was launched with prayer and trust in God. The network has remained true to its mission "to communicate the teachings and the beauty of the Catholic Church." People all over the world have been touched by the love and mercy of God through authentic Catholic programming.

   _____ In Irondale, Alabama in 1981, a Poor Clare nun, who was named Mother Angelica, built a Catholic cable television network, the Eternal Word Television Network (EWTN) on the grounds of her monastery, Our Lady of Angels Monastery, which is a very beautiful place. Building a television network is an expensive and technical task, and Mother did not know anything about television, but she prayed and trusted in God completely, and she succeeded. Mother established the mission of telling people all over the world about the teachings and beauty of the Catholic Church and the love and mercy of God.

Writing Effective Paragraphs Exercise

Here or on your own paper, write an effective paragraph about a person whom you know well (other than yourself) of at least four sentences. Use a strong topic sentence, lively verbs, and various sentence structures. Answers will vary.

Proofreading

Your writing cannot be effective if it contains errors. Proofreading is what writers do after editing or revising. Proofreading and editing might sound like similar terms, but they are different. Revising, or editing, involves significant rewriting of the paragraphs; for instance, changing the order of ideas, or adding transitions.

We don't proofread until we are sure that no further major changes are necessary. This is common sense. If you are going to delete an entire sentence, the sentence doesn't need to be proofread. So revise your rough draft and when you are satisfied with it, then you may begin to proofread.

Proofreading is a precise and careful examination of written work in order to find technical errors, such as misspellings and missing punctuation. When you proofread, you must read each word as it is and read slowly. You can't look for all errors all at once. This means that you will have to proofread more than once. For instance, look only at punctuation on the first reading. Then look only for spelling errors on the second reading. As you get better at proofreading, you can look for two elements at a time. Otherwise, read for one element only.

Here is a checklist of common errors:

- spelling, especially homonyms
- punctuation
- sentence fragments
- its and it's
- subject-verb agreement
- pronoun agreement
- missing or doubled words

Do not proofread for longer than fifteen minutes at a time. Proofreading requires intense concentration and can strain your eyes.

PROOFREADING SPELLING AND MISSING WORDS EXERCISE

Read the following paragraph once and correct it once for spelling errors. Then read it again to correct it for missing words. This paragraph is an excerpt from an essay called "The Geese" by E. B. White.

I have had pair of elderly gray geese—a goose and a gander—living on this place for number of years, and they have been my friends. "Companions" would be a better word; geese are friends with no one, they badmouth everybody and everything. But they are companionable once you get used to there ingratitude and there false accusations. Early in the spring, a year ago, as soon the ice went out of the pond, my goose started to lay. She laid three eggs in about a weak's time and then died. . . . I think this goose's time had come, and she had simply dyed of old age.

Additional proofreading exercises are scattered throughout the rest of the lessons.

Transitions

Transitions are words, phrases, sentences, or paragraphs that guide the reader. Use transitions when the reader needs help to see relationships between ideas, when you want to summarize or introduce what you are about to tell the reader, when you change scenes or the sequence of time events, or when you want to bring your writing to an end. These are places where the reader needs guidance.

Adding transitions lets the reader know that what follows is similar to what came before.

Examples:
additionally
furthermore
similarly
also
moreover

Contrasting transitions indicate that what follows is different from what came before.

Examples:
conversely
however
in contrast
nevertheless
on the other hand
still
while

Illustrating transitions indicate that an example is about to follow.

Examples:
specifically
for instance
in other words
that is
for example
in this case
to illustrate

Time transitions assist the reader with the order of events.

Examples:
immediately
soon
later, much later
after, afterwards
then
next
on the following day
first, second, third

Concluding transitions signal that the end of the writing is fast approaching.

Examples:
finally
in conclusion
lastly
hence
thus
therefore
as a result
consequently

COMPOSITION

LOCATING TRANSITIONS EXERCISE

Underline the transitions in the following paragraphs taken from Tolkien's The Hobbit.

1. "None to be seen by this moon," said Elrond, and he gave the map back to Thorin; and then they went down to the water to see the elves dance and sing upon the midsummer's eve.

The next morning was a midsummer's morning as fair and fresh as could be dreamed: blue sky and never a cloud, and the sun dancing on the water. Now they rode away amid songs of farewell and good speed, with their hearts ready for more adventure, and with a knowledge of the road they must follow over the Misty Mountains to the land beyond.

2. Gandalf in the meantime was still standing outside the door, and laughing long but quietly. After a while he stepped up, and with the spike on his staff scratched a queer sign on the hobbit's beautiful green front-door. Then he strode away, just about the time when Bilbo was finishing his second cake and beginning to think that he had escaped adventures very well.

3. Now we will return to Bilbo and the dwarves. All night one of them had watched, but when morning came they had not heard or seen any sign of danger. But ever more thickly the birds were gathering. Their companies came flying from the South; and the crows that still lived about the Mountain were wheeling and crying unceasingly above.

4. In the end he would only take two small chests, one filled with silver, and the other with gold, such as one strong pony could carry. "That will be quite as much as I can manage," he said.

Using Transitions Exercise

Write transitions in the blanks provided to connect the sentences. Use the suggested list of transitions below.

Suggested Transitions

consequently	first	moreover
for this reason	therefore	for example
in addition	to illustrate this	third
my second point is that	as a result	in conclusion
finally	for instance	first
however	nevertheless	

Speech given by the King of Epicuria at the Unified Conglomerated Incorporated Association of Countries:

"The learned representative from Megalohyperia has kindly explained why he believes no sovereign nation under 50 square miles should be allowed to exist. Larger is better is the motto of Megalohyperia. _____ we Epicurians must respectfully disagree. We submit the following three points regarding size. _____ a small size does not automatically indicate that something is of no consequence. _____ dynamite comes in small packages. _____ a tiny virus can fell a large beast with ease and rapidity.

_____ a country exists for the good of the citizens. This purpose has no bearing upon the size of a country because a small country can benefit its citizens. _____ in Epicuria, the citizens know their leaders and often take tea with them. Not all at once, of course. Can a large country provide this degree of sociability? Do the citizens of Megalohyperia even know the names of their leaders? I think not. _____ what is the reason for the limitation of 50 square miles? Why should the small countries be held to that standard? Why not 55 or 155 square miles? Why have countries at all? Why not unite every country into one all-encompassing union of humanity?

Countries are not merely lines on a map that can be withdrawn or redrawn because of a whim. One's country is one's home with definite boundaries that matter greatly whether the boundaries encompass much or little space. The feeling is the same for much or for little because that space is one's own. _____ I recommend that this proposal be withdrawn immediately and eternally."

Essays: Pre-writing Stage

The standard essay is a five to seven paragraph assignment that supports a main thesis. You will be expected to write standard essays throughout your middle school, high school, and college years. Why? Written essays show your ability to choose a topic, research the topic, organize your thoughts, and express your original thinking.

Essays focus on particular topics, but your first task is not to begin writing the essay. You need to do some pre-writing work first. To begin, find a suitable topic. Sometimes the assignment mentions a topic, but often you will have to narrow a broad topic down to a manageable size.

Example:

The topic is greyhounds. This is too broad. In a five to seven paragraph essay, you can't possibly tell everything about greyhounds.

Narrow the topic down to any of the following:

The Training of a Young Racing Greyhound
The Off-Track Life of a Racing Greyhound
The Dangers of Greyhound Racing
What Happens to Greyhounds at the End of Their Racing Careers
Preparing to Adopt a Greyhound
The History of Greyhounds

NARROWING DOWN A TOPIC EXERCISE

List at least three options for each broad topic. Research ideas for this exercise online or at your library. Answers will vary, but suggested answers are provided in the answer key. Save your work because you will use these options in another exercise.

Example: Trains
1. The History of the Baltimore and Ohio Railroad
2. The Ballad of Casey Jones
3. Smokey Mountain Train Vacation

A. Volcanoes

1. _____

2. _____

3. _____

B. Mathematics

1. _____

2. _____

3. _____

C. St. Francis of Assisi

1. _____

2. _____

3. _____

Why are You Writing This Essay?

O nce you have your topic narrowed down, do you immediately begin writing? No, you decide why you are writing the essay. What is the purpose for writing the essay? You should express this in one sentence. Later, you will use this sentence of purpose to develop a thesis statement for your essay.

Essays can be expository, narrative, persuasive, or creative.

An expository essay will explain, describe, or define a topic.

Examples: I will explain how to prepare to adopt a greyhound so that people will be knowledgeable about these animals and their special needs.

I want to define the characteristics of a greyhound so people will understand the beauty of this ancient breed of dog.

A narrative essay tells a story, which is usually a personal experience, and relates this story to a universal truth.

Examples: Chesterton narrated his adventure of sitting in a meadow and drawing with colored chalks on brown paper to illustrate the significance of colors and virtue.

E. B. White offers insight into possessions and territory when he writes about his experiences moving out of a New York apartment.

A persuasive essay argues a position in order to encourage the reader to accept that position as the right or correct one.

Examples: I describe the difficult conditions that racing greyhounds must endure so that people will not attend greyhound races.

A pro-life advocate writes an essay to persuade citizens to take a stand against capital punishment.

A creative essay often uses the writer's imagination and so may be somewhat fanciful, usually to entertain the reader or to stand out.

Examples: Mark Twain wrote a humorous essay on the difficulties he encountered while trying to learn to speak German.

Students who write college admissions essays want their essay to stand out, and so they may use nonstandard essay formats, humor, predictions, and other imaginative elements.

PURPOSE OF THE ESSAY EXERCISE

Using the three topics in the previous exercise, write a purpose statement for one of your narrower topics under Volcanoes, Mathematics, and St. Francis of Assisi. You will use the purpose statements in another exercise.

Example: I am going to describe a train vacation through the Smokey Mountains because I would like to share the advantages and disadvantages of a train vacation with others who might be considering taking one.

1. Volcanoes

   _____

   _____

   _____

   _____

2. Mathematics

   _____

   _____

   _____

   _____

3. St. Francis of Assisi

   _____

   _____

   _____

   _____

Main Thesis

Your purpose for writing will determine your main thesis, which is the main idea or position of your essay. You will have to describe, define, explain, narrate, or argue your main idea. In addition, you must have enough information (three to five points) to explain, narrate, or prove your thesis. Each of these points will require at least one paragraph.

Let's look at some thesis statements.

Greyhounds are an ancient breed, recognized in many countries by the nobility. *This thesis statement should be followed by dates and examples of special recognition by nobility in Egypt, in Persia, and in England.*

Retired racing greyhounds have special needs and need special consideration from new owners. *The essay should continue with an explanation of those needs and the requirements of adoption agencies.*

Any wild animal that I want to photograph will only appear when I've forgotten my camera. *This lengthy essay will cover story after story (some stories may be slightly exaggerated) of uncooperative deer, snakes, rabbits, armadillos, and raccoons that I have not been able to photograph.*

FIND THE MAIN THESIS EXERCISE

Underline the sentence that contains the main thesis in the following paragraphs.

"You can't turn back the clock" is a saying that I have often heard. I don't believe it. Every autumn, we do turn back the clock. Why? We must turn the clock back because we have moved it forward in the spring for Daylight Saving Time to take advantage of the longer days of summer. Benjamin Franklin thought of it first.

Make and bake bread in the shape of your favorite flower. That's right, use your favorite flour to make an edible flower. Please, try one of our morning glories with honey for breakfast. How about a daisy sandwich for lunch? Would you like to dip a sunflower into your tomato soup for supper? Follow these simple steps.

You may have run across B.C.E. in academic or newspaper writing and wondered what it meant. B.C.E. stands for Before the Common Era. We should not replace B.C. in our dating system with B.C.E. The reason given for using B.C.E. is misleading. Let's take a closer look at this reason.

MAIN THESIS EXERCISE

Look back at your purpose statements. Use these three statements to write three main thesis statements on your own paper. Answers will vary. Save these thesis statements as you will use them again.

Proofreading for Punctuation Exercise

Read the paragraphs once and correct punctuation errors. Read the paragraphs again and correct spelling errors. This paragraph is taken from Pope Benedict XVI's book Jesus of Nazareth. *The editors of this book chose not to capitalize divine pronouns, so do not correct the pronouns referring to God or Jesus.*

Now, it is true that this leds to the grate question that will be with us throughout this entire book: What did Jesus actually bring, if not world piece, universal prosperity, and a better world What has he brought?

The anser is very simple: God He has brought God. He has brought the God who formerly unveiled his countenance gradually, first to Abraham, then to Moses and the Profets, and then in the Wisdom Literature—the God who revealed his face only in Isreal, even thorough he was also honored among the pagans in various shadowy disguises. It is this God, the God of Abraham Isaac and Jacob the true God whom he has brought to the nations of the earth

Developing Your Point

You have a purpose and a thesis statement, yet you still have to explain, narrate, or prove your thesis. That may mean providing a list of steps, arguing a point, or describing and explaining. The next three to five paragraphs contain the details of your essay.

Example:

Retired racing greyhounds have special needs and need special consideration from new owners.

Point 1: Retired racers cannot be left outside unsupervised because they have no protection from the heat or cold. Most greyhounds have little fat and their fur is thin. In addition, a racing greyhound will probably have bald spots on its rump because of thin bedding. If you are hot or cold, your greyhound is probably feeling the extreme in temperature more than you are. Greyhounds are more susceptible to heatstroke than people are.

Point 2: Set up a crate before you bring your retired racer home because greyhounds will feel vulnerable and anxious if they do not have the familiar safety of a crate. They spend most of their racing careers locked inside one, so they view a crate as their space. Leave the door unlocked, and don't be surprised if your greyhound goes immediately into the crate and stays there for two or three days.

Point 3: Buy and use only a Martingale collar on your greyhound. A greyhound's head is narrow, and a regular collar will not stay. A greyhound must be leashed whenever it leaves a building because greyhounds are trained to chase a mechanical rabbit around a track. Therefore, they may impulsively streak after any moving object.

Point 4: Greyhounds have notoriously bad teeth. A racing diet is intended for strength and speed and not good dental health. To improve its dental health, feed your retired greyhound hard dog food with only the occasional soft treat. You may have to wean the greyhound off of soft food gradually.

Point 5: Greyhounds do not know how to play or guard a house. They are bred and trained with one purpose in mind: to win races. You can teach your greyhound to play, but you must be patient. They are not used to dog toys or playing fetch. However, they will enjoy lots of ear scratching and conversation. Furthermore, they may run away from strangers, and many greyhounds do not bark.

COMPOSITION

LOCATING POINTS EXERCISE

Place a check ✓ *by the points that could be used to prove the thesis statement. The statements are all true, but not all are proof of the thesis.*

Thesis: The historical evidence indicates strongly that Shakespeare was raised Catholic at a time when being Catholic was treasonous.

1. _____ Some of Shakespeare's neighbors in Stratford-upon-Avon were Catholic and had to speak carefully for fear of spies.

2. _____ Mary Arden, the mother of Shakespeare, was related to a network of Catholics who were implicated in various real-life plots against the Crown: the Throckmorton Plot, the Parry Plot, the Essex Rebellion, and the Gunpowder Plot.

3. _____ John Shakespeare (who was the father of William) wrote a spiritual testament of his Catholicism, in which he hoped for the sacrament of Extreme Unction.

4. _____ William Byrd, a Catholic who lived a double life, was Queen Elizabeth's court musician.

5. _____ Shakespeare purchased the Blackfriars Gatehouse in London, which was used before and after his purchase as a hiding place for priests and as a site for secret Masses.

6. _____ Many of Shakespeare's closest friends in London and in Stratford were fined or jailed for being Catholic.

7. _____ Seventy years after his death, an Anglican clergyman wrote that Shakespeare had died a papist, that is, a Catholic.

8. _____ Many Catholics hoped that the death of Queen Elizabeth would bring an end to the persecution of Catholics.

9. _____ Susanna Shakespeare, who was given control of Shakespeare's estate in his will, was fined for not complying with the regulations of Anglicanism, as her grandfather had been previously fined for noncompliance.

A Cohesive Essay

You have dealt with some of the pre-writing work, but there is still much work to be done. You have a topic, which has been narrowed down. You know why you are writing the essay, and you have a thesis statement. But what is missing?

Your thesis statement needs to be introduced properly. Next, you want to include the points in a logical order, and then conclude your essay with a summary or an interpretation of the significance of your thesis. Remember effective paragraphs? Effective paragraphs are what you need to write a complete essay that is unified from beginning to end.

The introductory paragraph engages your reader's attention and introduces the main thesis. The next three to five paragraphs prove or explain your thesis. The conclusion wraps up your essay. It should not always be a restatement of the introduction. You may be used to writing only a summary or restatement of the introduction. However, as you continue with your education, your writing instructors will expect more interpretation and insight in your writing. An insight shows your perception and understanding of the subject. An essay should have forward movement although you can and should refer to the main thesis throughout. The conclusion makes your position secure. It includes your final interpretation or insight into the significance of your main thesis.

Yet something is still missing. Most essays require research. If you are writing a narrative, research could consist of searching your memory to re-experience the event so that you can tell the story clearly. If you are writing an expository essay, double-check your facts by asking an expert, looking up definitions, and reading from reliable source material. If you are writing a persuasive essay, look at both sides of the argument because a strong argument takes the opposition into consideration.

The following is an example of a cohesive essay with comments in italics.

Example:

Hans Christian von Baeyer said, "Just because they lived long ago doesn't mean they were stupid." Von Baeyer is a professor of physics who obviously isn't arrogant. From our vantage point, we have the tendency to rank anyone no longer living as ignorant. We rarely consider what a debt we owe to the intelligence of those whom we may unconsciously imagine as primitive and ignorant savages. Let's consider only three out of many examples of the inventions and discoveries of those who lived long ago.

I'm introducing my topic with an appropriate quotation. The main thesis is the next to the last sentence in the introduction. I found the quotation in a science book while researching for another topic. I knew this quotation might be useful so I made a note of it, but I double-checked it by finding another source online.

Writing was necessarily invented by primitive people who were open to new ideas and yet illiterate: no one could read until writing was invented. Imagine the necessary leaps of intelligence that were needed to invent writing. This picture can stand for this thought. What next? Now we can put pictures together to take thoughts out of our mind and out of the sounds of our speaking and make them stand still. Then we can hand this writing over to someone else who can understand, and we don't have to remember word for word. Our messages and meaning won't get mixed up. Furthermore, we can send a message into the future. Let's hope that those future people are intelligent and well educated enough to understand us.

My first point is the topic sentence and the first sentence of the paragraph. I expand upon the topic sentence relating back to my thesis. I had already researched this point, and I'm recycling my research for this essay.

How could we live without wheels? Wheels of all sizes make modern life possible from watches to spacecraft. No one knows who invented the wheel. Perhaps it was some tired hunter or water carrier or firewood cutter who needed an easier way to make a living. Rolling a cargo of meat, water, or firewood home takes much less energy than carrying it with brute strength alone. Yet the inventor probably was some country bumpkin toughened by manual labor since few labor-saving devices had yet been produced. Long ago, without intending it, the inventor or inventors of the wheel began an extraordinary mechanical revolution that strongly influences us today. We are closely bound to their ingenuity even though we have modified and perfected it over the years.

The second sentence is my topic sentence. Again, I refer to the main thesis that the inventor must have been primitive by our standards. Yet the invention is not primitive but advanced. We still use the wheel. I researched some of this information online at a science web site.

The domestication of our supply of food ranks as an excellent idea. We know that no university professor thought it up. No, it must have been a primitive and probably illiterate group of nomads who didn't have wheels yet. Imagine if we were still nomads, traveling by foot from place to place, as the food supply dictated. At some point, some ignorant yet clever person or persons unknown made a profound connection: seeds can be planted and animals can be tamed to provide an abundant supply of food all year round. As a bonus, we can even ride some domesticated animals so that we don't have to walk everywhere. Unlike animals, we can take an active part in creating and protecting our own food supply.

The first sentence is the topic sentence. I draw back in the idea of illiteracy and the lack of technology (wheels). I taught and discussed this concept while substitute teaching only the week before writing this, so the content was still fresh.

Long ago, without the aid of textbooks or computers, without a history of inventions to build upon, primitive people changed the world with their inventions of writing, of the wheel, and of the domestication of our food supply. Maybe they didn't have nice clothing or indoor plumbing, but without their intelligence and effort, we wouldn't either.

The conclusion wraps up the points. Primitive people changed the world in significant ways that we benefit from. The closing insight points out that we wouldn't have a modern world without their primitive ingenuity.

To keep my essay cohesive (unified), I used repetition of certain words: primitive, long ago, ignorant, imagine, intelligence, writing, wheel, and food supply.

SENTENCE FRAGMENTS PROOFREADING EXERCISE

Read the paragraph once to look for and correct sentence fragments. Then read the paragraph again to find missing words. There is another error in this passage. Can you find it? This paragraph is from Simply Shakespeare *by Toby Widdicombe.*

Remember above all that Shakespeare wrote to be understood. You need to reject outright the elitist notion that Shakespeare is so complex in his language. That he is best discussed by experts for the betterment of other scholars. If that were case, the playwright then and now would have seen his works played before empty houses. It is true that the more you know the more appreciate. Shakespeares talent, but Shakespeare was and always has been quite accessible.

Completing the Pre-writing

You haven't researched your topic yet. Research is the one element of writing that many people put off and sometimes never do. You can learn to enjoy research, or you can continue not liking it, but complete the research regardless of your likes and dislikes. Some professional writers in recent years have been publicly humiliated and fired for failing to research. So getting a bad grade is not the only possible result of failing to research. Research is a matter of integrity and charity. Be honest with your readers and respect their time and their intelligence.

WHERE TO LOOK EXERCISE

Check ✓ which source would be appropriate for researching the following topics. More than one source may be appropriate.

Example: Caring for a Greyhound

   ✓   veterinary doctor

   _____   person who likes cats

   _____   someone who wishes to adopt a greyhound

1. The Life of G. K. Chesterton

   _____   your best friend

   _____   Dale Ahlquist, President of The American Chesterton Society

   _____   *The Autobiography of G. K. Chesterton*

2. How to Operate a Locomotive

   _____   an electrical engineer

   _____   a civil engineer

   _____   an experienced train engineer

3. Sources of Information for a Writing Project

_____ a librarian

_____ a writing instructor

_____ a book about researching for writing

4. How to Brush Your Teeth on the Space Shuttle

_____ a dentist

_____ NASA web site

_____ a space shuttle astronaut

5. Was Shakespeare Catholic?

_____ *The Catholicism of Shakespeare's Plays*, 1997

_____ *Shakespeare the Papist*, 2005

_____ *The Quest for Shakespeare: The Bard of Avon and the Church of Rome*, 2008

Research Exercise

Review your purpose statements and main thesis statements that you completed earlier and saved. Review the explanation and examples of developing your points.

After your review, choose one main thesis of the three you wrote earlier. Research this thesis. Find at least two sources of information to develop three to five points related to your thesis. On your own paper, write the name of the sources and brief notes about your points.

Drafting Stage

In this stage, you are writing a rough draft, designing the basics of your essay. Write as quickly as you can without worrying about spelling or punctuation. Get your thoughts down. Use the following two exercises to get started on your rough draft.

THINKING EXERCISE

Jot down your answers to these questions.

What is my purpose?

_____

_____

_____

How will I achieve this purpose? Will I use expository, narrative, persuasive, or creative writing?

_____

_____

_____

What is my main thesis?

_____

_____

_____

What are my basic points?

_____

_____

_____

_____

_____

_____

Do I have enough research to write about each point?

_____

_____

_____

How can I engage my reader in the first sentence of my essay?

_____

_____

_____

Drafting Exercise

Using the Thinking Exercise, write an introduction to your essay on your own paper. Then develop each point into a paragraph. Finally, write your conclusion.

Revision Stage

Do not proofread your draft yet for punctuation and spelling errors. Revise for cohesiveness and content first. The next exercise will walk you through the revision process.

READING YOUR DRAFT EXERCISE

Read your rough draft aloud. Ask yourself these questions:

1. How does it sound? Awkward or smooth?

2. Does it make sense as a whole essay?

3. Is the beginning clear and easy to follow? Did you use transitions?

4. Is each point clear and developed?

5. Did you use lively words? Count your use of forms of the verb "to be." Can you replace any of these with stronger verbs?

6. What questions might a listener or reader ask you about the essay?

7. What are the strong points of your essay?

8. What are the weak points?

CONTENT REVISION EXERCISE

Revise your rough draft based upon your answers to the questions above.

Subject-Verb Agreement Proofreading Exercise

Read the paragraph once to correct for subject-verb agreement. A single subject requires a single verb, and a plural subject requires a plural verb. Read the paragraph again and look for two other types of errors.

Across the dark skies flies the storm clouds. Lightning strikes. Half the trees in the forest appears briefly in the eerie flash. The children shiver inside their tent. Will storm pass over them? They wait and listen, other campers are scuttling into their tents. Another flash brightens the skies, and several echoing thunderclaps resounds.

Proofreading Your Revision Exercise

Read your first revision carefully. Proofread for these areas:

1. Spelling

2. Punctuation

3. Consistent verb tense

4. Missing words

5. Sentence variety

6. Transitions between ideas

Make necessary corrections.

Publishing and Presenting Your Essay

Create a clean copy of your essay. A clean copy means writing that contains no mistakes and that is easy to read. Either type and print it or handwrite it neatly.

If you are using a computer, you may decide to add an image to your essay. If you are handwriting the essay, you may want to draw a cartoon or picture to illustrate your essay.

Present your essay to an audience. You have spent time and effort on behalf of an audience. Remember that you wrote your essay for a reason. Now is the time to present your essay to your audience.

You may present your essay for a grade, for publication online or in print, or aloud to a live audience.

Reports

Follow the same process of pre-writing, drafting, rewriting, and proofreading for other types of writing, such as reports. Students are often assigned book, science, and history reports. A report provides students with the opportunity to research a topic thoroughly, organize information, and then present the information to educate others. Reports are factual writing although you may also present informed opinions and interpretations or theories since there are few subjects that are thoroughly known. We are always finding out more and correcting previous errors.

Sometimes the topic is assigned to you, and sometimes you will choose your own topic. In the following exercises, the topic is to describe three learning styles (visual, auditory, and tactile/kinesthetic) and criticisms of the concept of learning styles.

We first want the definitions or descriptions of the three learning styles. Where can we look for this information? Because we are working with definitions and descriptions, begin by looking up the phrase "learning styles" in a current dictionary. This phrase was not used until the 1970s, so if your dictionary is not up to date, you won't be able to find the word.

Then look for visual learner, auditory learner, and tactile/kinesthetic learner. Are these words in the dictionary? Probably not, but check the dictionary first.

SOURCES FOR REPORTS EXERCISE

What other sources could we use? Check ✓ the sources that would be appropriate.

_____ encyclopedia from 1965

_____ encyclopedia from 2005

_____ teachers, especially elementary level

_____ commercial web site selling a learning styles inventory

_____ university web site discussing research into learning styles

_____ homeschooling veterans who have taught several children

_____ book or article written by researcher discussing experiments with learning styles

_____ podcast or video of an overview of learning styles

_____ random opinions about learning styles on the Yahoo Answers web page

Proofreading Exercise

Read the following paragraphs carefully at least three times. Correct the errors. The paragraphs are from Manalive by G. K. Chesterton. Do not correct the word "manalive" or place commas between the list of names (all of which are spelled correctly) the voice in the tree gives.

Arthur Inglewood has seen a figure jump from a wall into a tree and he is trying to determine if that figure is actually his friend Innocent Smith.

"Who is there?" shouted Arthur. Who are you, are you Innocent?"

"Not quite," answered a obscure voice among the leaves. "I cheated you once about a penknife."

The wind in the garden had gathered strength and was throwing the tree backwards and

forwards with the man in the thick of it, just as as it had on the gay and golden afternoon when he

had first arrived.

"but are you Smith?" asked Inglewood as in an agony.

"Very nearly," said the voice out of the tossing tree.

"but you must have some real names," shriek Inglewood in despair. "You must call yourself

something."

"Call myself something," thunder the obscure voice, shaking the tree so that all it's ten thousan

leaves seemed to be talking at once. "I call myself Roland Oliver Isaiah Charlemagne Arthur

Hildebrand Homer Danton Michelangelo Shakespeare Brakespeare—"

"But, manalive!" began Inglewood in exasperation.

"That's right! That's right!" came with a roar out of rocking tree; "that's my real name."

More Sources Exercise

Use index cards or regular lined paper to begin gathering information and taking notes from the following sources. Use the example as a model. Always note the source material. Readers should be able to find your sources to check your facts.

Example: Learning Styles from Dictionary.com—an individual's mode of gaining knowledge, esp. a preferred or best method

Learning Styles from Wikipedia.com—Write the description. Take notes on criticisms of learning styles. *Some teachers will not allow use of Wikipedia as a source. We are using Wikipedia and other sources, so we will be able to double-check our facts.*

Learning Styles from another encyclopedia either in print or online—write the description. Take notes on criticisms of learning styles. Take notes on visual, auditory, and tactile/kinesthetic if this information is provided.

Learning Styles from a science or educational web site—take notes on information regarding visual, auditory, tactile/kinesthetic learning. Look for information on criticism of learning styles.

Interviewing Sources

Conduct interviews to get a range of opinions from people who are actively involved in your topic. You may interview people face-to-face, by phone, by mail, and by e-mail.

Never conduct an interview without preparing a list of specific questions. In addition, explain your topic to the person being interviewed. Follow these steps to conduct an interview that respects the time and knowledge of the person being interviewed:

1. Do preliminary research first through print and online sources.

2. Create a list of three to seven specific questions to ask. These questions should be open-ended questions instead of yes and no questions.

3. Find the appropriate person to interview. You may want to interview more than one person.

4. Introduce yourself and explain your assignment. Ask for permission to interview. If you are meeting face-to-face, set up an appointment and be on time and prepared.

5. Conduct the interview. Take notes if you are meeting face-to-face or by telephone.

6. Thank the person for taking time to assist you with your assignment.

CREATING INTERVIEW QUESTIONS EXERCISE

You are conducting an interview regarding criticism of learning styles. Look at each pair of questions. Write "Yes" for the best question in each group.

Example: _____ Have you ever been interviewed about this topic before?

_____Yes_____ What caused you to investigate learning style theory?

1. _____ How widely used are learning styles?

   _____ Are learning styles used in elementary schools?

2. _____ Based upon your experience, how would you define learning style?

   _____ Do you have a preferred learning style?

3. _____ Are some learning style tests more reliable than others?

   _____ What is the major weakness of a learning style test?

4. _____ Based upon your experience, is there a best method for learning?

   _____ Could you describe briefly how people learn?

5. _____ What disadvantage do you see in teaching based upon learning styles?

   _____ Should teachers teach using only one method?

6. _____ What is the future of teaching based upon learning styles?

   _____ Do you think the idea of learning styles will become obsolete within the next ten years?

Interview Exercise

Choose one person to interview regarding learning styles. You may choose someone who believes and uses learning styles or someone who is critical of learning styles.

Write three to seven questions.

Interview the person and take notes if necessary. One advantage to interviewing people by e-mail and mail is that the person will write the responses, but you may have to wait longer to get your information because writing takes time.

Be sure to thank the person granting you the interview.

Organizing Information

By now you have lots of notes, and yet notes are not enough. You need to organize your information.

Do you have enough information to write your report? Maybe and maybe not.

Organize your notes or index cards. You may want to rewrite information to place it in these categories:

1. Definition of Learning Styles
2. Visual Learners
3. Auditory Learners
4. Tactile/Kinesthetic Learners
5. Criticisms of Learning Styles

Which areas have little information? Where can you go for more information? You need enough information to write at least one paragraph on each of the five categories. These categories form a basic outline and logical order for your report.

Do further research if your organization indicates that you need more information. You may request help from a librarian, do more online research, or conduct another interview.

Drafting Your Report

Write a rough draft of your report on learning styles. Use the standard format of an introduction, supporting paragraphs, and a conclusion.

In your introduction, describe what the assignment is. What is the purpose of your report?

Use the five categories to write your supporting paragraphs. Write at least one paragraph for each category, but you may have enough information to write more than one paragraph for some of the categories, such as Criticisms of Learning Styles.

Write a brief conclusion to summarize the information you reported. You are not analyzing the information. You are presenting the information in this particular report, so you may conclude with a summary of the information. Some reports, such as a science lab, may require an analysis or interpretation of the information presented.

Proofreading Exercise

Your writing will not always be as full of errors as these proofreading exercises have been. Sometimes only one or two errors may be hiding in your writing. (Or perhaps none at all.) Read this slightly shortened paragraph from E. B. White's essay "Coon Tree." Make corrections if necessary. There are no comma errors, and bedchamber is spelled correctly.

I think this is the fourth spring the coon has occupied the big tree in front of the house, but I have lost count. She is like a member of our family. She has her kittens in a hole in the tree about thirty-five feet above the ground, which places her bedchamber a few feet from my bedchamber but at a slightly higher elevation. It strike me as odd (and quite satisfactory) that I should go to sleep every night so close to a litter of raccoons. The mother's comings and goings are as much a part of my life at this season of the year as my mourning shave.

Revising Your Report

Many reports rely on research, and report writers should always tell the reader where the information was found. You can easily include the information in the report.

Examples:

According to Dictionary.com, the definition of a learning style is "an individual's mode of gaining knowledge."

In the *Encyclopedia Britannica,* the article "_____" written by _____ describes learning styles as . . . .

During an interview with Professor Frank Coffield, he indicated that . . . .

Your readers need to know where the information is coming from. Use quotation marks when you are quoting directly, but don't fill up your report with quotation marks, or it will look messy, and your writing instructor will ask you to put the information in your own words to make sure that you understand the information.

IN YOUR OWN WORDS EXERCISE

Rewrite each quotation in your own words on your own paper. You may need a dictionary to look up some of the words used in the quotations. Answers will vary.

Example: From Dictionary.com—"an individual's mode of gaining knowledge, esp. a preferred or best method"

> Dictionary.com defines a learning style as a person's way of gaining knowledge, particularly when the person uses one way in preference to other ways.

1. From a web site article "Learning Styles" — "Many educational psychologists believe that there is little evidence for the efficacy of most learning style models."

2. From Learning-styles-online.com —"If you use the visual style, you prefer using images, pictures, colors, and maps to organize information and communicate with others."

3. From the book *Becoming a Middle School or High School Teacher in Texas* by Janice L. Nath, 2005 —"Finally, teachers must understand that students who have a preference for a particular style are sometimes not well served by schools."

4. *University of Utah Tips for Tactile Learners* —"Make rearranging items a physical activity (don't draw connecting arrows—put them on separate cards to physically rearrange)."

5. From Shannon Hutton, M.Ed., School Counselor— "Parents should also try to give directions verbally, paraphrase key information, provide students a quiet place to do homework, and play music softly in the background, if they prefer."

Revising Exercise

Read your report aloud.

1. Is the information clear?

2. Do you need to provide examples of each learning style?

3. Do your sentences follow logically from one idea to another?

4. Did you use lively words? Count your use of forms of the verb "to be." Can you replace some of these with more precise verbs?

5. Is each category adequately described, or does one category dominate the others by including much more information?

6. Did you indicate within the report where you found the information?

Proofreading Exercise

Look over your report carefully more than once. Check the following elements as you look at each word and each sentence:

1. Spelling
2. Punctuation
3. Consistent verb tense
4. Missing words
5. Sentence variety
6. Transitions between ideas

Make the necessary corrections. Create a clean copy of your report.

Presenting Your Report

Choose one of the following ways to present your report:

1. Read it aloud to a group of at least four other people and discuss. The group may be your family or a homeschooling support group or a class.

2. Submit your written report to a homeschooling web site, newsletter, or magazine.

3. Present your report to a group, using at least one large image. Do not read your report aloud, but use note cards for your presentation.

4. Present your report as a slideshow presentation to a group. This method calls for giving only the essential information and adding images. You will have to choose key elements that you want to share with the group and base your slideshow upon only these key elements.

COMPOSITION

Responding to Literature

Writers write stories, novels, and poetry to provoke a response from their readers. They expect their writing to touch the reader intellectually, emotionally, or spiritually. Learning how to respond to literature in writing and through oral discussion takes you on a deeper journey into the story or verse.

In order to respond to literature, we usually have to read the work more than once. The first reading gives us a general idea of the surface of the work. What is the work about? Who are the characters? What is the setting? What happens? The second reading allows us to discover the details and the craft in the writing. Why did the writer choose a particular metaphor or simile? What is the meaning behind the words? Is there irony? What universal truth is the writer presenting?

G. K. Chesterton said, "The aim of good prose words is to mean what they say. The aim of good poetical words is to mean what they do not say." His statement means that we must read prose—which is the language used for stories, essays, and reports—and poetry by understanding that these two types of writing use a different approach.

Prose is usually clear-cut language in a straightforward conversational style. Poetry makes words dance. The poet considers the sound of words, the relationship of one word to another, and the rhythm of words.

READING EXERCISE

Read Joyce Kilmer's poem aloud. Listen for the rhythm, the sound of the words, and the basic subject of the poem.

Not on the lute, nor harp of many strings
   Shall all men praise the Master of all song.
   Our life is brief, one saith, and art is long;
And skilled must be the laureates of kings.
Silent, O lips that utter foolish things!
   Rest, awkward fingers striking all notes wrong!
   How from your toil shall issue, white and strong,
Music like that God's chosen poet sings?

There is one harp that any hand can play,
   And from its strings what harmonies arise!
There is one song that any mouth can say,—
   A song that lingers when all singing dies.
When on their beads our Mother's children pray
   Immortal music charms the grateful skies.

Poetry Comprehension Exercise

Answer the following questions on your own paper. Use complete sentences.

1. What is the poem about?

2. Is the rhythm fast, slow, or in-between? (Should the poem be read quickly or slowly? If you are not sure, try reading the poem aloud at different speeds.)

3. What is a lute?

4. What does laureate mean?

5. Who is the "Master of all song"?

Reading Further Exercise

Kilmer's poem on the previous page is called "The Rosary." Read "The Rosary" again silently. During this reading, look at the details of the writing. Answer the following questions on your own paper. Use complete sentences.

1. What particular comparison does Kilmer use throughout the entire poem? He compares prayer with what art?

2. Why does he make this comparison?

3. What emotions does Kilmer refer to?

4. Does this poem change the way you think about prayer? How?

C O M P O S I T I O N

Reading "The Sparrow and the Hare"

Read the following story from Aesop's Fables twice. At the end of the fable is a brief explanation of Aesop, the original fable-teller, and the elements of a fable.

One bright fall morning, a plump hare was nibbling the seeds in an open meadow and hopping from one bite of food to another. The hare's long ears flicked back and forth. A sparrow perched in a tree at the edge of the meadow was chirping and waiting for insects to fly by.

A shadow passed over the meadow unnoticed by the hare and the sparrow who were attending to their breakfast. Suddenly, an eagle fell upon the hare, clutching it tightly and tearing at it. The eagle had found its breakfast.

"Ahhh!" the hare cried out in fear and pain.

Approaching the scene, the sparrow scolded the hare, saying, "Why were your feet so slow? I thought you were always alert and as swift as the air itself. But now you are caught. That will teach you to pay attention instead of greedily stuffing your belly."

The eagle began to carry off the hare, and the sparrow followed, intending to say more. However, as the eagle and the sparrow rose in the air, a hawk swooped upon the sparrow and killed it before it could again open its beak.

And all was then silent in the meadow on that bright fall morning.

Aesop lived long ago and was a slave who apparently had the gifts of wit and storytelling. Life in ancient Greece, especially the life of a slave, was harsh with many difficulties and inconveniences. Aesop would not have written down his fables but told them aloud to others who remembered them and retold them.

Fables are a particular type of writing with a specific purpose. A fable teaches a moral truth by means of a short memorable story, using animals and objects that may speak or otherwise act as humans would or might. Using animals and other objects in this way is called anthropomorphism. The prefix "anthropos" refers to human and "morph" means change. This anthropomorphism is a unique element in fables, so keep that in mind when you write about fables.

DESIGNING QUESTIONS ABOUT THE FABLE EXERCISE

Create five to seven questions about the fable and answer them. Be sure to include at least three questions that go beyond the surface of the story.

Writing about the Fable

Before you begin writing, here is an example of a written response to another fable "The Old Man and Death," in which Death is personified and allowed to speak.

"The Old Man and Death"

An old laborer, bent double with age and toil, was gathering sticks in a forest. At last he grew so tired and hopeless that he threw down the bundle of sticks, and cried out: "I cannot bear this life any longer. Ah, I wish Death would only come and take me!"

As he spoke, Death, a grisly skeleton, appeared and said to him: "What wouldst thou, Mortal? I heard thee call me."

"Please, sir," replied the woodcutter, "would you kindly help me to lift this faggot of sticks on to my shoulder?"

Fleeting Emotions in "The Old Man and Death"

In Aesop's fable "The Old Man and Death," a worker becomes tired of looking for wood in the forest. He is old and tired of his life of labor. Perhaps he has been working for long hours and his muscles ache with fatigue. He feels hopeless and overwhelmed by work. So he cries out for death. He feels ready for an end to his life. Yet when Death appears unexpectedly in response to his cry, the old man's feelings change immediately and dramatically. Instead of carrying through with his desire for death, he asks death to assist him by placing the wood back on his shoulders. The old man has quickly decided that he can find the hope and the strength to continue his life of labor.

This fable illustrates that our emotions are powerful but often short-lived. Weariness and other strong unpleasant emotions make us do and say things we don't really mean. Emotions can make us thoughtless and reckless, but situations causing these emotions rarely last long, so we would be wise not to allow our emotions to rule us.

The first paragraph describes the events of the fable in relation to the topic of fleeting emotions. It also names the emotions experienced in the fable and describes the feelings of the man further. The first paragraph ends with the significance of the old man's decision.

The second paragraph relates the meaning of the story in universal terms. Aesop must have experienced exhaustion as a slave. Emotions are common to all people in all times.

This is not the only way to write a response to literature, but we are using this simple format to give you practice.

Proofreading Exercise

Read and make corrections if necessary to this paragraph.

Knowledge provides answers to questions and mysteries. However, often knowledge begets more questions and mysteries. Some scientists spent years arguing for the Steady State Theory because they didn't like the idea of our universe having a beginning. This model of the universe accepts the evidence that space is expanding outward, nevertheless, the model rejects that the universe may not have existed at some point in time. Yet evidence against this theory mounted because of discoveries in astronomy and physics. Georges Lemaître, Catholic priest and scientist, proposed the idea that the universe began as perhaps a single atom, the primordial atom, that expanded. This new idea, later named the Big Bang Theory, brought new questions and mysteries. Why did the atom, now referred to as a singularity, expand? Scientists believe that it was infinitely hot, infinitely dense, and infinitely small. Can finite humans find a solution to the question of infinity?

Writing about "The Sparrow and the Hare" Exercise

1. Choose one of your questions (see p. 219) and develop it into a two-paragraph response to the story. Use the example given on page 220 as a model.

2. Be sure to title your response.

3. Use present tense verbs to write about the fable. Yes, stories are written in past tense, but we use present tense when we respond to literature in writing.

4. In the first paragraph, relate the details of the fable in connection with the question you chose to explore.

5. Use the second paragraph to indicate the significance of the answer to your question in universal terms.

Read your response aloud. Are you satisfied that you have written what you intended? If not, then revise. If you are satisfied, then proofread the paragraphs.

Narrative Writing

Narrative writing tells a story in a series of events. This happened first, and then that happened and so on. The series of events is called the plot of a story. The story may be written, spoken, danced, or sung. Poems can be narrative and fables are narrative. A mystery story depends upon a series of events in a particular order. The poem "The Rosary" is not a narrative poem because there is no sequence of events. So you can determine whether an essay, a poem, or any writing is narrative by deciding whether the writing contains a sequence of events that need to be understood in time order.

Time in Narratives

While knowing the time order when events occurred in narrative writing is important, the writer has choices. The writer can begin at the end of the story and tell the ending first. Or the writer may begin at an exciting event in the middle of the story and fill the reader in on the beginning later on. And the writer may begin at the beginning and tell the events in order as they occurred. Remember your previous practice with transitions? Transitions help the reader understand when an event took place, especially if the story does not begin at the beginning.

Most narrative stories are told in past tense. This does not mean that every verb will be in the past tense, but the writer indicates that the events have already happened and are now being related to the reader. A story could be written in the present tense, but this can be awkward sounding and doesn't allow the writer the freedom that using past tense does. Relating a story that has already happened allows the writer to begin at any point in the story. If you write in present tense, you must write as the story unfolds.

(When we write about literature, we use present tense verbs. This is the custom. So write your stories in the past tense, but write **about** stories in the present tense.)

Developing a Series of Events in a Narrative

Beginning writers may not be sure which events to include in a story. Some events can be left out, but other events should be included to make the story realistic, to keep the story flowing, and to develop the plot.

Examples:

If a story depends upon a key being found, the existence of this key needs to be introduced into the story towards the beginning even if the writer doesn't tell the reader how significant the key is.

To emphasize a character's troubles, make the character's weaknesses apparent in the beginning. A person who doesn't know how to survive in the wilderness will have more obstacles to overcome than a Boy Scout who has his badges in Camping and Wilderness Survival. You will stress the details and steps involved as the person without knowledge tries to find shelter, water, and food.

SERIES OF EVENTS EXERCISE

Write in the missing details for each series of events. Answers will vary.

Example: found a recipe, bought ingredients, <u>*prepared the recipe*</u> , ate

the food

1. climbing down stairs, was distracted by dog, _____ , fell

   down the stairs, family heard noise and rushed to help

2. _____ , mounted the horse, rode out of the stable into

   the countryside

3. worked at odd jobs, saved money, _____ , gave the gift

   to my mother

4. called dog, put leash on dog, encouraged dog to get in car, drove to vet,

   _____

5. mother asked me to look after baby, picked up baby,

   _____ , baby fell asleep

6. found mysterious old key in attic, showed key to parents, tried key in different locks,

   _____

Deciding the Series of Events

Which events you choose depend upon the kind of narrative you wish to tell. A mystery story needs clues. A biography needs important life events. An adventure story needs exciting events. Most stories need events that show how the main character changes.

DECIDING EVENTS EXERCISE

On your own paper, list at least five events that would be appropriate to include in the following types of narratives. Answers will vary, but suggested answers are provided in the answer key. Save your list because you will use it in the next exercise.

1. Science Fiction

2. Journal of a Prisoner of War (either fictional or real)

3. Your Autobiography

4. Fictional Account of a Shipwreck

Choosing the Order of Events Exercise

On your own paper, explain when you would begin each story—in the beginning, in the middle, or at the end—using the four types of narrative given above and your list of events from the last exercise. Explain why you would begin your story at that point. Answers will vary, but suggested answers are provided in the answer key. Save your work as you will be using it to write a story after working with dialogue.

Example: Detective story—I would begin this story at the beginning with the crime being committed so that the detective could examine the crime scene and begin looking for clues to explain why the crime was committed and who the guilty party was.

Proofreading Exercise

Read these paragraphs twice and make corrections if necessary. This excerpt is from The Elements of Style *by William Strunk, Jr. and E. B. White. Do not correct the first sentence, which is a sentence fragment. Famous authors are allowed to write sentence fragments. Alas, beginning writers are not.*

Clarity, clarity, clarity. When you become hopelessly mired in a sentence, it is best to start fresh; do not try and fight your way through against the terrible odds of syntax. Usually what is wrong is that the construction has become to involved at some point; the sentence needs to be broken apart and replaced by two or more shorter sentences.

Muddiness is not merely a disturber of prose. It is also a destroyer of life, of hope: death on the highway caused by a badly-worded road sign, heartbrake among lovers caused by a misplaced phrase in a well-intentioned letter, anguish of a traveler expecting to be met at a railroad station and not being met because of slipshod telegram. think of the tragedies that are rooted in ambiguity, and be clear! When you say something, make sure you have said it. The chances of your having said it are only fare.

Dialogue in a Story

Dialogue is what characters say aloud in a story. Writers use dialogue for several reasons. Dialogue can keep the story moving, reveal characters' emotions and thoughts, show conflict, provide information to the reader, and engage the reader in the story.

Listening

Eavesdropping means listening to someone's **private** conversation. So avoid doing that because it is wrong. However, there are many **public** conversations that you can listen to in order to learn how to write dialogue. Listening to movies, family conversation, interviews, and speeches will give you an idea of how people talk.

LISTENING EXERCISE

For this exercise, listen to at least three natural, unplanned conversations. Do not engage in the conversation. Take notes if possible and listen for these elements:

1. Who is dominating the conversation?

2. Is the other person listening?

3. What kind of sentences or words are people using—short one-word answers, half sentences, or long precise sentences?

4. Does the speaker have definite speech patterns? Are certain words repeated? Does the speaker prefer large words or slang? How precisely does the person speak? Is the speech hurried or slow?

Please see the answer key for suggested answers and additional information about natural conversations.

Much of what we say in unplanned natural conversations is empty talk. We're not imparting critical information, but we are recognizing each other's presence and being civil and expressing our opinion. We are not attempting to forward a plot or show conflict or provide information to a reader. For this reason, writers do not often write completely realistic dialogue. They don't have a lifetime to get their story told. Writers have to be selective and plan dialogue.

You can use some elements of natural conversation, such as casual language and individual speech patterns, in your writing. When you write dialogue, you want each character to sound unique. Your characters should not all sound alike.

Listening to a Scripted Dialogue Exercise

Listen to a scene from a movie at least twice. Take notes on these elements:

1. Who is dominating the conversation in the scene?

2. How is the other person responding?

3. What is the speech pattern for each person engaged in the conversation?

4. What is the purpose of the conversation—moving the plot forward, revealing the character, showing conflict, providing information to the viewer, engaging the viewer in the action? *The dialogue can have more than one purpose.*

5. How does the writer achieve this purpose? What elements of the conversation contribute to fulfilling this purpose?

COMPOSITION

Purpose of Dialogue Exercise

Determine at least one purpose—moving the plot forward, revealing the character, showing conflict, providing information to the viewer, engaging the viewer in the action—for the following dialogues.

1.   Thorin, leader of a company of dwarves, is making a speech:
"We are met to discuss our plans, our ways, means, policy and devices. We shall soon before the break of day start on our long journey, a journey from which some of us, or perhaps all of us (except our friend and counselor, the ingenious wizard Gandalf) may never return. It is a solemn moment. Our object is, I take it, well known to us all. To the estimable Mr. Baggins, and perhaps to one or two of the younger dwarves … the exact situation at the moment may require a little brief explanation—"
   —*The Hobbit* by J. R. R. Tolkien

Purpose(s) of dialogue _____

2.   "I don't believe you," broke out his companion, not without agitation. "I've heard you had some bad habits—"
"All habits are bad habits," said Michael, with deadly calm. "Madness does not come by breaking out, but by giving in; by settling down in some dirty, little, self-repeating circle of ideas; by being tamed. *You* went mad about money, because you're an heiress."
   "It's a lie," cried Rosamund furiously. "I was never mean about money."
   "You were worse," said Michael … "You thought other people were."
—*Manalive* by G. K. Chesterton

Purpose(s) of dialogue _____

3.   Father Brown is discussing a case with an artist and a detective:
   "A person *can't* be quite alone in a street a second before she receives a letter. She can't be quite alone in a street when she starts reading a letter just received. There must be somebody pretty near her; he must be mentally invisible."
   "Why must there be somebody near her?" asked Angus.
   "Because," said Father Brown, "barring carrier-pigeons, somebody must have brought the letter." —"The Invisible Man" by G. K. Chesterton

Purpose(s) of dialogue _____

   Where should you place dialogue in your story? Write dialogue for situations where people would normally speak. Not too many people speak in the elevator or on a crowded train. People do speak when they are surprised, when they meet someone, when they need help, when they play with a pet, and on many other occasions.

Writing Dialogue Exercise

Find the time order list you saved from your previous exercises (see p. 225). You have already chosen a beginning point for each of the four story possibilities. Select one of the four stories and write a dialogue for the beginning scene. If the beginning scene would not be appropriate for a conversation, then review your list of five events for each narrative, and write dialogue for one of those events.

Writing Your Story

You have now practiced two key elements in writing narratives: time order and dialogue. Apply what you have learned and continue writing more of your story. Use your list of events to continue your story. Aim to include a series of three events that would logically follow one after the other.

You may wish to research your ideas for events to make the narrative more realistic. Use your imagination as well.

Revise your narrative at least once. Then proofread and present your story to an audience.

COMPOSITION

Answer Key

p. 2

Writing Subjects Exercise

Answers may vary.

1. The moon
2. (Person's name)...He/She
3. Mother/Father
4. (person's name)
5. The sky...rain...(person's name)

p. 3

Writing Predicates Exercise

Answers may vary, but each predicate must contain at least one verb.

1. ...enjoyed ramming the walls with its head.
2. Over the mountains hiked...
3. ...slept.
4. ...splashed in the pool...
5. ...snapped the flags.
6. ...played soccer...
7. ...cheerfully greeted an unexpected visitor.

p. 4

Subjects in Questions Exercise

1. the fir tree
2. Who
3. you'd ('d represents the verb "would" and is not part of the subject)
4. no one
5. it

p. 5

Predicates in Questions Exercise

1. Is, tall or short, or dark or fair
2. Does, sit on a stool or sofa or chair
3. Does, sleep on a mattress, a bed or a mat, or a Cot
4. Does, cross his t's and finish his i's with a Dot
5. Do, like him extremely well

p. 7

Sentence Fragment Exercise

1. subject
2. predicate
3. predicate
4. subject
5. subject
6. predicate

p. 8

Independent Clauses or Not Exercise

1. IC
2. SF
3. SF
4. SF
5. IC
6. IC
7. SF
8. IC
9. IC
10. IC

p. 9

Understood Subjects Exercise

1. Understood
2. Understood
3. Understood
4. Fragment
5. Understood
6. Understood
7. Fragment
8. Fragment
9. Understood

p. 10

Review of Subjects and Predicates

1. Marcus, Aurelia, turned punctually
2. Are, still awake
3. you
4. reminded them to say their prayers, The children, the white rat, George Jaworski

p. 12

Simple or Compound Exercise

1. SS
2. CS
3. SS
4. CS
5. CS
6. SS
7. CS
8. CS
9. SS
10. SS
11. CS
12. SS

p. 13

Mixing Simple and Compound Sentences Exercises

Answers may vary.

The raccoons scooted. **Two blurs of black and gray streaked out through the kitchen door, and I closed it.** My sister shook her head. We both sighed. **This was one big mess, but that wasn't the whole problem. Our friends were coming over in thirty minutes, and we had promised to make hotdogs for them. The hotdog package was ripped, while half the hotdogs were missing.** Where were the hotdog buns? **The catsup was lying on the floor, and the bottle had shattered.** Would we be able to keep our promise of hospitality to our friends?

232

p. 14

Compound Subjects Exercise

1. <u>Sr. Marie</u>, <u>Fr. Thomas</u>
2. <u>you</u>, <u>you</u>
3. <u>The baked fish with tomato sauce that we made for our Lenten supper</u>, <u>the lemon cake that was leftover from yesterday</u>
4. <u>The computer</u>, <u>Miss Millie Manor</u>
5. <u>Who</u>, <u>they</u>
6. <u>Kelly and Samuel</u>, <u>they</u>

p. 15

Compound Predicates Exercise

1. <u>knows the answer</u>, <u>doesn't even understand the question</u>
2. <u>was listening to Amadeus</u>, <u>was listening to Johann</u>
3. <u>were not making mud pies all morning</u>, <u>had to stop because we ran out of aluminum pie pans</u>
4. <u>Should</u>, <u>go swimming</u>, <u>would</u>, <u>rather play soccer today</u>
5. <u>is making an awful racket and seems irritated</u>, <u>is happily barking and jumping about under the cat's tree</u>

p. 17

Forming Compound Nouns Exercise

1. buttercup
2. peanut butter
3. supernova
4. grace note
5. almsgiving
6. sight singing, sight-singing is also common
7. forget-me-not
8. insight
9. goodwill
10. morning glory
11. mother-in-law
12. honeycomb

p. 18

Forming More Compound Nouns Exercise

1. dining room
2. bedroom
3. roommate
4. room temperature
5. goldsmith
6. golden rule
7. grasshopper
8. grass snake
9. White House
10. white-out
11. life cycle
12. lifetime

p. 19

Compound Nouns or Not Exercise

1. CN
2. CN
3. (adjective)
4. (adjective)
5. (verb)
6. CN
7. CN
8. (Walled describes the convent, but the two together do not form a compound noun.)
9. CN

p. 20

Hyphenated Compound Noun Exercise

<u>ear-ache</u> (earache is properly spelled as one word)
<u>rubber-ball</u> (rubber ball is properly spelled as two words)
<u>stable-floor</u> (stable floor is properly spelled as two words)

p. 21

More Compound Nouns Exercise

(*Starlight* may be used as a noun, but here it is used as an adjective.)
<u>fire-folk</u>
<u>circle-citadels</u>
<u>elves'-eyes</u>
<u>quickgold</u>
<u>whitebeam</u>
<u>Flake-doves</u>
(*farmyard* is used as an adjective here)
<u>May-mess</u>
<u>March-bloom</u>
(*withindoors* is used as an adverb)

p. 22

Review of Compound Sentences

1. ...beds, and...
2. ...balm, but... *To distinguish the second independent clause from the list of flowers, you may also use a semicolon.* ...balm; but...
3. We watered, we weeded. *Or* We watered, and we weeded.
4. ...earth, and the rain... *Or* ...earth; the rain...
5. ...bloomed, and...

The nine compound nouns are as follows:
springtime
flower beds
snapdragons
love-in-a-mist
bee balm
forget-me-nots
sunshine
Grandmother
birthday

p. 23

Singular Possessive Nouns Exercise

1. Peter's math book
2. Lucy's DVD
3. the dog's leash
4. Sr. Agnes's rosary, or Sr. Agnes' rosary
5. the O'Callaghan family's generosity

p. 24

Plural Names Exercise

1. Carloses
2. Joneses
3. MacIntoshes
4. Valdezes
5. Larches

p. 25

Plural Possessive Nouns Exercise

1. the children's Masses
2. the singers' voices
3. the horses' stalls
4. the Joneses' cars
5. the babies' tears
6. the Larches' badges

p. 26

Singular and Plural Possessive Nouns Exercise

<u>Stephen Hawking's book</u> *A Brief History of Time* is a best-selling science book, which was published on <u>April Fools' Day</u>, 1988. It's not easy to understand how such a book could become a bestseller. In chapter one, Hawking describes <u>Nicolaus Copernicus's model</u> of the universe, <u>Isaac Newton's laws</u>, and <u>Edwin Hubble's observations</u>. The Hubble Telescope, which has recorded beautiful images of the universe from its orbit around the Earth, is named after Edwin Hubble. Although the book explains complicated mathematical concepts, it contains only one equation, <u>Einstein's $E=mc^2$</u>. The information in later chapters is mind-boggling. What will be the physical <u>universe's fate</u>? Will the uncertainty principle lead some scientists to be more open-minded about <u>God's dominion in the universe</u>? Hawking mentions the <u>Catholic Church's views</u> and actions in several places in this book. Science and faith aren't always comfortable in <u>each other's company</u>, but as stated in <u>Pope John Paul II's encyclical</u> "Faith and reason are like two wings on which the human spirit rises to the contemplation of truth; and God has placed in the human heart a desire to know the truth."

p. 27

Writing Possessive Nouns Exercise
Answers will vary.

1. (Teresa's Bible) singular possessive
2. (the sisters' closet) plural possessive (two or more sisters share a closet)
3. (Mom's purse) singular possessive
4. (the Valdezes' piano) plural possessive
5. (the Davises' dog) plural possessive
6. (the Littles' Christmas tree) plural possessive

p. 28

Collective Nouns Exercise

1. <u>company</u>
2. classes
3. <u>family</u>
4. <u>jury</u>
5. <u>troupe</u>
6. <u>crew</u>
7. <u>hosts</u>
8. <u>Plagues</u>

p. 29

Matching Collective Nouns and Members Exercise

muster of peacocks
exaltation of larks
fall of lambs
cloud of grasshoppers
prudence of vicars
banner of knights
cortege of mourners
bench of bishops

p. 30

Creating Collective Nouns Exercise

Answers may vary.

an accompaniment of altar servers

a cacophony of thunderstorms/of uneducated minds/of owls

a beautification of virtues/of religious sisters

a blessing of religious sisters/of virtues/of holy days

a calendar of holy days

a confusion of uneducated minds/of thunderstorms

a wisdom of owls/of virtues/of religious sisters

p. 31

Appositives Exercise

1. The Eternal City (Rome)
2. a monument built around 315 A.D. to honor the triumph of Constantine at the Battle of Milvian Bridge (the Arch of Constantine)
3. The artist of the family (Marie)
4. The children's parents (Mr. and Mrs. Laurent)
5. her son (Christ)
6. One of the holiest Christian sites and the burial place of St. Peter (the Basilica)
7. parents and children (The Laurent family)

p. 32

Appositive or Not Exercise

1. Appositive (The movie trilogy)
2. Appositive (the hobbits)
3. Appositive (the heir of Bilbo)
4. (blank)
5. Appositive (a volcano in the midst of the stronghold of the enemy)
6. (blank)
7. Appositive (the enemy of all that is good and beautiful in Middle-Earth)

p. 33

Writing Appositives Exercise

Answers will vary.

1. type of animal/pet's name
2. the Big Apple / home of the New York Yankees
3. the head of the Catholic Church/ Benedict XVI
4. the founder of the Missionaries of Charity/ a well-known religious sister
5. cherry cheesecake/carrot cake/ pineapple upside down cake

p. 34

Review of Nouns

1. collective noun
2. appositive
3. plural possessive noun
4. singular possessive noun
5. appositive
6. collective noun
7. plural possessive noun

p. 35

Using Linking Verbs Exercise

(is smell ~~appears~~)

(is ~~was am~~)

(~~felt~~ feel ~~feeling~~)

(was ~~seemed appeared~~)

(proved ~~seemed remained~~)

(looks ~~smells am~~)

(~~have~~ remain ~~become~~)

p. 36

Completing the Linking Verb Exercise

Answers may vary.

1. the study of facts about the physical world/a subject we study
2. genius/physicist/scientist/winner of the Nobel Prize
3. genius/physicist/scientist/winner of the Nobel Prize
4. chemist/scientist/physicist/ Nobel Prize winner
5. scientist/physicist/Nobel Prize winner
6. mother/father/scientist/Nobel Prize winner

p. 37

Linking Verb or Not Exercise

1. LV
2. LV
3. LV
4. AV
5. LV
6. AV
7. LV
8. AV
9. LV
10. AV

p. 38

Another Linking Verb Exercise

1. (none)
2. (none)
3. appear
4. become
5. seems
6. sounds
7. remain

p. 39

Writing Verbs Exercise

Answers may vary.

1. spin/sway/shout
2. tipped/dumped/poured
3. exploded/erupted
4. eat/bake/serve
5. spill/drop/pour
6. Finish/Complete
7. gathered/stood/kneeled

p. 39

Locating Action Verbs

Skim

fling

Bathe

ebbs

p. 41

Locating Helping Verbs Exercise

1. are (helping)
2. have been (raking)
3. would, would (rake, take)
4. was (spilling)
5. have been (trimming)
6. will (fit)
7. Should (start)

p. 42

Contractions and Helping Verbs Exercise

1. are
2. will
3. do
4. will, are
5. have (been is also a helping verb)
6. should
7. am

p. 43

Review of Verbs

V

HV, LV

HV, V, V

HV, V

HV, V, V

V, HV, LV

p. 44

Past, Present, or Future Tense Exercise

1. Past
2. Present
3. Past
4. Past
5. Past
6. Past
7. Past
8. Past
9. Future
10. Present

p. 45

Writing Verb Tenses Exercise

Answers may vary.

1. will climb
2. are climbing/climb
3. have climbed/climbed/had climbed
4. serves/is serving
5. baked/did bake/has baked
6. will eat
7. killed/had killed/have killed
8. are tracking/track
9. will kill/are going to kill

p. 46

Using Present Progressive Verbs Exercise

1. are traveling
2. are looking
3. is growing
4. is becoming
5. am wondering

p. 47

Finding Past Progressive Verbs

1. (none)
2. was ruling
3. were persecuting
4. was demanding, were holding
5. was summoning
6. (none)
7. was writing, was renting
8. (none)
9. (none)
10. was growing

p. 48

Writing Future Progressive Verbs

1. will be teaching
2. will be researching
3. will be discussing
4. will be tasting
5. will be photographing
6. will be preparing

p. 49

Past, Present, or Future Progressive Verb

1. Future, will be warming
2. Present, are sleeping
3. Future, will be waking
4. Past, was snuffling
5. Past, were fiercely striking
6. Present, am walking
7. Past, was singing
8. Present, is challenging
9. Present, is watching

p. 52

Completing the Verb Forms Exercise

1. rung
2. thought
3. wear
4. quit
5. said
6. spend
7. thrown
8. been
9. did
10. break

p. 53

Regular or Irregular Verbs Exercise

1. R; enjoy
2. I; do, did, done
3. R; enchant
4. I; know, knew, known
5. I; write, wrote, written
6. I; be, was/were, been
7. R; call
8. I; tell, told, told
9. R; chant

p. 54

Review of Verb Tenses

1. am catching.
2. sings.
3. trampled.
4. were speaking.
5. will tell.
6. kept.
7. will be remembering.
8. think.
9. swam.
10. cut.

p. 55

Finding Transitive Verbs

1. <u>encountered</u>
2. <u>boarded</u>
3. <u>had</u> thoughtfully <u>packed</u>
4. <u>touched</u>
5. <u>ate</u>
6. <u>met</u>
7. <u>knew</u>

p. 56

Writing Transitive Verbs Exercise

1. will plant, <u>tomato seedlings</u>
2. bathes, <u>the elephants</u>
3. are watching, <u>the marathon</u>
4. heated, <u>soup</u>
5. was tracing, <u>the historic route</u>
6. grades, <u>the children's essays</u>
7. will swim, <u>the English Channel</u>

p. 57

Choosing Intransitive Verbs Exercise

1. swinging up high
2. playing in the sand
3. sleeping
4. barks loudly
5. standing near the sandbox
6. walking toward the swings
7. sit and swing with the older children
8. is napping

p. 58

Transitive or Intransitive Exercise

1. I
2. T
3. T
4. T
5. I
6. T
7. T
8. T
9. I
10. T

p. 59

Review of Verbs

1. <u>are dying</u> (HV I)
2. <u>sneezed</u> (I)
3. <u>is rumbling</u> (HV I)
4. <u>will paint</u> (HV T)
5. <u>are singing</u> (HV T)
6. <u>ate</u> (T)
7. <u>are</u> (LV)

p. 60

Finding Antecedents Exercise

1. <u>Mark's</u>
2. <u>Kim and Phyllis</u>
3. <u>rain</u>
4. <u>Dr. Jones</u>
5. <u>cat</u>
6. <u>Kate's</u>, <u>Zachary's</u>
7. <u>president</u>

p. 62

Choosing Subjective Singular and Plural Pronouns Exercise

1. They
2. She
3. he
4. They
5. I
6. We
7. It

p. 63

Choosing Objective Singular and Plural Pronouns Exercise

1. her
2. it
3. them
4. you
5. me
6. us

p. 64

Choosing Possessive Singular and Plural Pronouns Exercise

1. yours
2. Mine
3. Hers
4. ours
5. his
6. Yours
7. Ours
8. Theirs

p. 65

Finding Indefinite Pronouns Exercise

1. No one, several
2. Something, everyone
3. None
4. Many, few
5. Anything
6. Both, all
7. Each
8. something

p. 67

Choosing Reflexive and Intensive Pronouns Exercise

1. yourself
2. myself
3. itself
4. themselves
5. herself
6. himself
7. ourselves
8. yourselves

p. 68

Distinguishing between Reflexive and Intensive Pronouns Exercise

1. Reflexive, himself
2. Reflexive, herself
3. Intensive, themselves
4. Reflexive, themselves
5. Intensive, ourselves
6. Reflexive, ourselves
7. Intensive, yourself
8. Intensive, itself
9. Reflexive, yourselves

p. 70

Choosing Interrogative Pronouns

1. Which
2. what
3. Whom
4. Who
5. Whose
6. Who
7. Whom
8. Whose/which
9. Which/Whose

p. 71

Review of Pronouns

1. herself
2. What
3. Which/What
4. Everyone, Everybody, Anybody, Anyone
5. myself
6. you
7. mine
8. no one, nobody
9. myself
10. her
11. ours
12. theirs

p. 72

Choosing Adjectives Exercise

short
young
good-natured
shy
serious
polite
blond

p. 73

Finding Adjectives Exercise

Three, large, green, dense, hungry, cautious, strong, wise, three, fierce, angry, safest, other, two, lone

p. 75

Choosing Adverbs Exercise

1. Yesterday
2. Too
3. quietly
4. often
5. home
6. Here

p. 75

Adverb Relationships Exercise

1. looked over
2. dangerous
3. respected
4. would act
5. gave
6. shouted
7. climbed

p. 76

Another Adverb Relationship Exercise

1. confidently is modifying the verb jumped
2. often is modifying the verb shared
3. yesterday is modifying the verb skied
4. home is modifying the verb took
5. quite is modifying the verb tired
6. rarely is modifying the verb missed
7. most is modifying the verb skillful

p. 77

Review of Adjectives and Adverbs

1. Adjective, Adjective
2. Adverb, Adjective
3. Adjective
4. Adjective
5. Adverb, Adjective
6. Adjective
7. Adverb, Adjective
8. Adjective, Adverb

p. 78

Choosing Prepositions of Position Exercise

Answers may vary.

1. on/on top of
2. above/far from
3. along/up/down
4. down/below
5. on, below/beneath/under/by
6. above/over
7. into/inside

p. 79

Understanding Prepositions Exercise

1. manner
2. authorship
3. giving
4. time
5. position
6. direction
7. description
8. reason
9. description

p. 80

Finding Prepositions

1. in his heart, in his head
2. to the most obscure of all classes
3. of very rapid racing cars, to a standstill, in a block, of traffic
4. in front of him, behind him
5. Without authority

p. 81

Choosing Conjunctions Exercise

1. or
2. yet
3. and
4. so
5. nor
6. for
7. but

p. 82

Finding Conjunctions Exercise

1. Furl that Banner, for 'tis weary...
   For there's not a man to wave it,
   And there's not a sword to save it,
   And there's no one left to lave it...
   And its foes now scorn and brave it...

2. ...Built by never a spade nor pick
   Yet covered with earth ten metres thick...
   Never to laugh nor love again
   Nor taste the Summertime.
   For Death came flying through the air
   And stopped his flight at the dugout stair,
   Touched his prey and left them there...

p. 84

Choosing Interjections Exercise

1. Oh dear/Oh no
2. Oh no/Oh dear
3. Alleluia!
4. O
5. Um
6. Ah!

p. 85

Review of Prepositions, Conjunctions, and Interjections

1. O: Inter, O: Inter, of: Prep
   With: Prep, and: Conj
   and: Conj
   And: Conj, and: Conj, to: Prep, of: Prep
2. Ho: Inter, with: Prep
   or: Conj
   Or: Conj, or: Conj
   O: Inter, with: Prep

p. 90

Singular or Plural Subjects Exercise

1. Sing
2. Pl
3. Pl
4. Pl
5. Sing
6. Sing
7. Pl
8. Sing
9. Sing
10. Sing
11. Pl

p. 91

Singular and Plural Verbs Exercise

1. were
2. stood
3. were
4. was
5. did
6. healed
7. condemned

p. 92

Singular and Plural Subjects Exercise

1. we/I
2. he
3. I
4. I/We/You
5. we/you
6. It
7. You
8. He/It
9. She/He/It
10. We/They/I

p. 93

Editing Verbs for Collective Nouns Exercise

1. ✓
2. *dances* instead of *dance*
(Although the plural pronoun *they* takes the plural verb *go*, the subject *family* is singular and takes the singular verb.)
3. *sells* instead of *sell*
4. *is* instead of *are*
(*A raft* is singular.)
5. ✓
6. ✓
7. *meet* instead of *meets*
8. *were* instead of *was*
9. ✓

p. 95

Editing Verbs for Indefinite Pronouns Exercise

1. *are* instead of *is*
(Half in this case equals more than one cookie.)
2. ✓
3. ✓
4. *has* instead of *have*
(Each one has . . .)
5. ✓
6. ✓
7. *is* instead of *are*
8. *is* instead of *are*
9. *was* instead of *were*
10. ✓

p. 96

Review of Indefinite Pronouns

1. Sing; <u>Most</u>
(How many books? Only one book.)
2. Pl; <u>More</u>
3. Sing; <u>everyone</u>
4. Sing; <u>Everybody</u>
("Everybody" seems as if it should be plural, but think "every single body" or "each body" as one person, which is singular.)
5. Pl; <u>All</u>
6. Sing; <u>all</u>
("All" is referring to a single forest, not to the many maple trees that make up the forest.)
7. Pl; <u>many</u>
8. Pl; <u>Few</u>
9. Sing; <u>Less</u>
("Less" refers not to "them," but to "time.")
10. Sing; <u>neither</u>
("Neither" is the subject of the main sentence.)
11. Pl; <u>Several</u>
("Several" . . . "volunteered.")

p. 97

Review of Subject-Verb Agreement

<u>is</u> (singular)
<u>grants</u> (singular)
<u>pauses</u> (singular)
<u>is wearing</u> (singular)
<u>stands</u> (singular)
<u>wears</u> (singular)
<u>is hung</u> (singular)
<u>bank</u> (plural)
<u>keep</u> (plural)
<u>leaves</u> (singular)
<u>turns</u> (singular)
<u>seems</u> (singular)

p. 99

Objects for Lay Exercise

Answers will vary.

1. eggs
2. papers, books, pencils, scissors
3. axe, hose, gloves, ladder
4. feet, head, arms, legs
5. forks, spoons, knives
6. glasses, papers, keys, books
7. paws, feet

p. 100

Choosing Lay or Lie Exercise

1. lays
2. lay
3. lie
4. lay
5. lays
6. lie
7. lies
8. lay

p. 104

Deleting Troublesome Words Exercise

Grammatically correct sentences listed below.

1. If you want to be content in life, then you will practice charity.
2. To catch the thief quickly was their main goal.
3. The sick children would soon be all right because they received loving attention from their family.
4. The athlete was a swift runner.
5. The crowd inferred that the play had been cancelled when they could not open the doors to the auditorium.
6. Sudden fame had a ruinous effect upon her.
7. The habits of a rat are different from those of a gerbil.
8. Each ballerina found her dancing costume ready to wear because the staff had worked overtime.
9. The essays were well written as all essays should be.
10. Less than half the city is receiving rain.
11. Few of the books in their collection are leather bound.

p. 106

Choosing Grammatically Correct Words Exercise

1. regardless
2. Physically
3. infer
4. Fewer
5. fewer
6. his
7. farther
8. First
9. May
10. can
11. alternative
12. further

p. 108

Diagramming Exercise

1.

2.

3.

4.

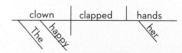

5.

p. 109

Diagramming Predicate Nouns and Predicate Adjectives Exercise

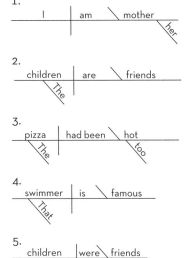

p. 110

Diagramming Compound Subjects and Compound Predicates Exercise

1.

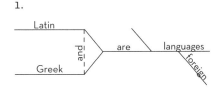

2.

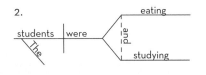

3.

4.

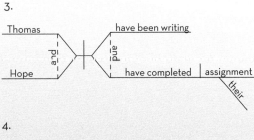

p. 116

Capitalizing Exercise

1. divinity
2. first letter of each line
3. personal title
4. pronoun I
5. title of a work
6. proper noun
7. relationship
8. proper noun
9. personal title
10. proper noun

p. 118

Using Commas Correctly Exercise

The incorrect sentences are corrected.

1. Correct
2. Incorrect (The babies were wrapped in pink, white, and yellow blankets.)
3. Correct
4. Correct
5. Incorrect (We bought green onions, yellow squash, red cabbage, and orange peppers for the meal.)
6. Incorrect (The costume designer drew three kinds of coats—gold and silver, white and pink, and yellow and blue.)
7. Incorrect (The Dicksons, the Carvers, and the Washingtons all play the piano beautifully.)
8. Correct

p. 119

Writing Commas Exercise

1. "Yes, Caroline," Edgar replied, "I planned to mow the grass, wash the windows, and trim the shrubs."
2. The Yard Machine, a recent purchase from the home improvement store, would not start.
3. "Caroline, the mower isn't working!"
4. Edgar gave the mower one last try, sighed deeply, and looked about for a bucket.
5. He found a yellow bucket, a plastic object with a large hole in the bottom.
6. "You can't possibly use that to wash the windows," Caroline said.
7. She added, "Edgar, I noticed that some birds are nesting in the shrubs."
8. Edgar decided that he would take the mower in for repairs, purchase a sturdy new bucket, and enjoy the sight of the nesting birds.

p. 123

Using Commas with Dependent and Independent Clauses Exercise
The choice of conjunctions may vary.

1. ...invented, people...
2. ...evident, **but/yet** the...
3. ...Daimler, **and** Americans...
4. ...cars, gasoline...
5. ...cars, **but/yet** not...
6. ...first, they...
7. ...techniques, **and** these...

p. 125

Review of Commas

Every sentence is correctly punctuated and should have a check mark by it.

ANSWER KEY

242

Photocopying of copyrighted material is strictly illegal.

p. 128

Using Colons Exercise

1. ...verses: Matthew 7:7, Mark 13:32, and Malachi 1:6...
2. (blank)
3. ...White: "You...
4. (blank)
5. ...Malone:
6. (blank)
7. (blank)
8. ...life: to learn...

p. 130

Review of Semicolons and Colons

1. separating elements in a list
2. separating a quotation and an independent clause
3. separating independent clauses
4. separating an appositive at the end of an independent clause
5. distinguishing the main title and the subtitle
6. distinguishing hours and minutes
7. separating a list from an independent clause
8. distinguishing chapter and verse

p. 135

Quotation Marks or Italics Exercise

1. "Love and Loyalty," Gilbert Magazine
2. Challenger
3. Beowulf
4. "Afghan Girl," National Geographic
5. "The Council of Elrond," The Lord of the Rings
6. Catholic Answers Live, "Miracle on the Hudson"
7. (no quotations or italics)
8. I Have a Dream
9. "Silent Night"
10. Catholic Culture
11. "Teaching My Dog to Roll Over"

p. 137

Adding Apostrophes Exercise

1. ...cook's skill...
2. Milan's grandmother...Lord's Prayer...
3. ...boys' spoons...
4. ...Dennis's applause...boys' balancing...
5. ...geese's reaction...ladies' hats...
6. ...ladies' shrieks...
7. ...Chris's spoon...Paul's lap.
8. ...Camposes' laughter... everybody's sides...

p. 138

Ownership Exercise

1. ...Francis's award-winning... Life's Mysteries... (One song and one apostrophe s; do not forget the apostrophe s for the name of the song)
2. Dave's and Mitzi's shoes... (Two pairs of shoes and two apostrophes)
3. A cat's and a dog's noses...
4. ...Nicholas's car...
5. ...Smiths' dog...
6. Patricia's and Donald's toothbrushes...
7. Karl's, Timothy's, and Paula's dogs...

p. 141

Possessive Pronoun Exercise

1. ✓
2. ✓
3. Whose, not Who's
4. its, not it's
5. ✓
6. ✓
7. another's, not anothers
8. ✓

p. 143

Contractions Exercise

1. I'm going...you're ready.
2. Who's supposed...
3. ...Singin' in the Rain.
4. It's got...
5. (no correction)
6. (no correction)
7. ...couldn't be...
8. 'Twas a...

p. 144

Review of Quotation Marks, Italics, and Apostrophes

1. ✓
2. (blank)
3. (blank)
4. ✓
5. (blank)
6. ✓
7. (blank)
8. ✓
9. (blank)
10. ✓
11. ✓
12. (blank)

p. 146

Hyphenating Compound Adjectives Exercise

1. ...nine-tenths...
2. ...heat-seeking...
3. ...forty-three...
4. ...solar-powered...
5. ...ten-minute...
6. Sixty-six...
7. ...left-handed...
8. (no hyphen needed)
9. ...broken-hearted...
10. ...eight-sided...

p. 149

To Hyphenate or Not Exercise

1. ...quasi-official...
2. ...fast-paced...
3. ...half-baked.
4. (no hyphen needed)
5. ...long-range...
6. ...forty-odd...
7. ...cross-legged...
8. ...Franco-Prussian...
9. (no hyphen needed)
10. ...self-restraint...

p. 151

Informal Dash Exercise

1. The day was sunny and bright—not a day on which you would expect the storm clouds of disaster to rain down upon you—and the birds were sweetly trilling on the lamp posts.
2. Whatever the children may have thought of asparagus soup—and they had often thought of feeding it to the dog—it was greatly appreciated by the adults.
3. "And you are implying—?" "That we will be late if you don't hurry."
4. time—the measured or measurable period during which an action, process, or condition exists or continues
5. That crazy mockingbird sat in the oak tree and belted out its songs—the tone of a cell phone, whistling, the cackle of a grackle, whining, and the roar of a lawn mower.
6. Musicians from around the globe—Hungary, Egypt, Ireland, Taiwan, Canada, and Honduras—enjoyed the international computer music conference.
7. I know that I have seen your face many times before, but I can't remember—

p. 153

Using Parentheses Exercise

1. ...(1786-1859)...
2. ...(compelled to join the military)...
3. No parenthesis
4. ...(his father was not happy when he discovered this situation some months later)...
5. ...(he struggled with Latin and failed the first examination).
6. ...(1) bishops, (2) priests, (3) religious brothers and sisters, (4) those in doubt about their vocation, and (5) great and small sinners...
7. No parenthesis

p. 155

Parentheses in Citations Exercise

1. ...(V.i.68-89)
2. ...(p. 119)...
3. ...(Loss of the Eurydice, lines 33-36)
4. ...(Pearce, p. 174).
5. ...(pp. 315-320)...
6. ...(Strunk and White, pp.75-76).

p. 157

Abbreviations Exercise

1. EWTN
2. Dr.
3. URL
4. BC
5. p.m.
6. Sr., Jr.
7. DVRs
8. mph
9. Fr., Sr.
10. KJV, NAB, RSV

p. 158

Understanding Abbreviations Exercise

1. European Union
2. American Automobile Association
3. Bachelor of Arts
4. barbeque
5. Central Intelligence Agency
6. disc jockey
7. deoxyribonucleic acid
8. Great Britain or Gigabyte
9. Fahrenheit (referring to temperature)
10. Internal Revenue Service
11. Monsignor
12. South
13. Registered Nurse
14. parts per million

p. 160

Latin Abbreviations Exercise

1. against
2. note well, pay attention
3. i.e.
4. R.I.P.
5. AMDG
6. re
7. for example
8. in the work or author cited previously
9. et. al.
10. after what has been written
11. v.v.
12. in the same place, author
13. by the grace of God
14. etc.

p. 163

Writing Numbers Exercise

1. Forty-nine instead of 49
2. C
3. zero instead of 0
4. 951 instead of nine hundred fifty-one
5. one-third instead of $^1/_3$
6. C
7. C
8. ten million instead of 10,000,000

p. 165

Time Exercise

1. 8:45 p.m.
2. 12:00 noon
3. (All answers would be correct.)
4. Three-thirty in the morning
5. 3:30:49.
6. half-past
7. quarter after

p. 166

Review of Dashes and Parentheses

1. C
2. dash: —Socrates
3. parentheses: ...(1) electrons, (2) protons, and (3) neutrons.
4. dash: ...this instant—after... (This is an ironic and therefore emphatic interruption because the speaker is not leaving this instant.)
5. dash: FAQ—Frequently Asked Question
6. C
7. C
8. parenthesis: ...ruled (lines 1-2).
9. dash or parenthesis: Socrates—the horse, not the philosopher—enjoyed rolling in the grass. (Parentheses are okay if you are not emphasizing the ironic use of the name Socrates.)
10. parenthesis: ...agreeable" (*Hill*, p. 162).

p. 167

Review of Abbreviations and Numbers

1. a.m.
2. AT&T
3. Two-thirds
4. two
5. 16
6. miles per gallon *or* mpg
7. in. (Remember that the abbreviation for inches requires a period to avoid confusion with the preposition.)
8. 5,117
9. 1-5 (*One through five* would be okay, but using numerals is usually easier, especially for double and triple digit numbers.)
10. St. *or* Saint
11. 9
12. midnight

p. 171

Word Choice Exercise

1. Formal
2. Formal
3. Informal
4. Formal
5. Informal
6. Informal
7. Formal

p. 172

Finding Clichés Exercise

1. <u>for a song</u>
2. <u>money can't buy happiness</u>
3. <u>melted in my mouth</u>
4. (No clichés)
5. <u>to burst your bubble</u>
6. (No clichés)
7. <u>didn't have a leg to stand on</u>

p. 173

The Sound of Being Exercise

My dog <u>was</u> a racing greyhound. His name <u>was</u> Hi Warlock, which is too fierce a name for his sweet disposition. He <u>is</u> now called Lock, which <u>is</u> not the best name for him, but it <u>is</u> better than Hi Warlock. We <u>are</u> happy to have adopted Lock because he <u>is</u> a great housedog. He <u>is</u> quiet and obedient. He <u>is</u> our favorite dog. *(This paragraph also suffers from too many topics. The topic changes from the name of the dog to his behavior.)*

...Because he <u>was</u> timid and frightened...

p. 173

To Be or Not To Be Exercise
Answers will vary.

Many people around the world enjoy cooking. Everyone who lives in the country of Epicuria cooks with the greatest gusto. This country is filled with enthusiastic cooks. Some Epicurians specialize in baking crusty loaves of bread and rolls. Some prepare all kinds of pasta from scratch. Some grill delicious meats over an open fire. Many Epicurians, particularly those who are too young to use an oven or stove, create tasty tossed salads. Those Epicurians—you will often discover them eating and sharing food with friends.

p. 175
Sentence Variety Exercise
But as I sat scrawling...behind.
(Long complex sentence that begins with a dependent clause, contains a short interruption, and a long appositive)

I searched...chalk.
(Short yet compound sentence)

Now, those who...positive and essential.
(Long complex sentence which uses three restrictive clauses and parentheses for an interruption and several prepositions in a series)

I cannot avoid remarking here upon a moral significance.
(Short sentence with a preposition)

One of the wise and awful truths...a colour.
(Complex sentence with restrictive clauses)

It is not a mere absence...as black.
(Compound sentence using comparisons)

p. 177
Indicating the Topic Exercise
There was a wedding in town this winter. (The topic is marriage.)

No rain has fallen in several weeks. (The paragraph is about dry weather.)

p. 181
Effective Paragraphs Exercise
1. __ It was the funniest thing we ever saw...
(*This paragraph is too repetitive without giving many details. It's simplistic with little variety. Simply telling your reader that something is funny doesn't make it so.*)

   ✓ Tom invited me to his house...

2. ✓ E. B. White preferred to understate rather than overstate...

   __ When he wrote, E. B. White used understatement often...
(*This paragraph is a mish-mash of ideas. It changes the topic and gives vague information. Vague information is not effective.*)

3. ✓ Mother Angelica made up her mind to build a Catholic television...

   __ In Irondale, Alabama in 1981, a Poor Clare nun...
(*The first sentence is too long. The reader will have difficulty figuring out what the main idea is. The last sentence does not clearly tie in the mission with the television network.*)

p. 183
Proofreading Spelling and Missing Words Exercise
...had **a** pair of...
   for **a** number
...to **their** ingratitude...
...and **their** false...
...soon **as** the ice...
...about a **week's** time...
...simply **died** of old age.

p. 185
Locating Transitions Exercise
1. and then
The next morning
Now
2. in the meantime
After a while
Then
just about the time when
3. Now we will return to Bilbo and the dwarves.
when morning came
4. In the end

p. 186
Using Transitions Exercise
Some answers may vary.
However/Nevertheless
First
For instance/for example
Moreover/In addition
My second point is that
For example/To illustrate this
Third/Finally
In conclusion/For this reason

p. 188

Narrowing Down a Topic Exercise
Answers will vary. These are
suggestions for topics.

A. Volcanoes
1. Where Volcanoes Are Located
2. Mauna Loa's Most Recent
Eruption
3. What is Lava?

B. Mathematics
1. Using Manipulatives to Learn
Fractions
2. Day in the Life of a Math
Professor
3. Math Anxiety

C. St. Francis of Assisi
1. The Early Life of Francis
2. Italy During the Time of St.
Francis
3. St. Francis and Animals

p. 193

Find the Main Thesis Exercise

The thesis statement does not
have to be the first sentence in an
introductory paragraph as you can
see from these examples.

We must turn the clock back
because we have moved it forward
in the spring for Daylight Saving
Time to take advantage of the longer
days of summer.

Make and bake bread in the shape
of your favorite flower.

We should not replace B.C. in our
dating system with B.C. E.

p. 194

Proofreading for Punctuation
Exercise

...this **leads** to...

...the **great** question...

...world **peace**, universal...

The **answer** is...

...simple: **God. He** has...

...the **Prophets**, and...

...in **Israel**, even **though** he...

...of **Abraham, Isaac, and Jacob, the**
true God, whom he...

p. 196

Locating Points Exercise

1. (blank)
2. ✓ (This is not an especially
strong proof, so it may remain
unmarked.)
3. ✓
4. (blank)
5. ✓
6. ✓
7. ✓
8. (blank)
9. ✓

p. 199

Sentence Fragments Proofreading
Exercise

...his **language that** he is...

...were **the** case...

...more **you appreciate**
Shakespeare's talent...

p. 200

Where to Look Exercise

1. **The Life of G. K. Chesterton**
your best friend *(only if your best*
friend is an expert on the subject)
Dale Ahlquist, President of The
American Chesterton Society
The Autobiography of G. K.
Chesterton

2. **How to Operate a Locomotive**
an experienced train engineer

3. **Sources of Information for a**
Writing Project
a librarian
a writing instructor
a book about researching for writing

4. **How to Brush Your Teeth on the**
Space Shuttle
NASA web site *(This question is*
frequently asked.)
a Space Shuttle Astronaut *(first-*
hand experience)

5. **Was Shakespeare Catholic?**
The Catholicism of Shakespeare's
Plays, 1997
Shakespeare the Papist, 2005
The Quest for Shakespeare: The
Bard of Avon and the Church of
Rome, 2008
(These books are all in favor of
Shakespeare's Catholicism. You
would want to read the opposing
view as well.)

p. 204

Subject-Verb Agreement

Proofreading Exercise

...dark skies **fly** the...

...forest **appear** briefly...

...will **the** storm...

...and **listen. Other campers** are...

...thunderclaps **resound**.

p. 206

Sources for Reports Exercise

___ encyclopedia from 1965
(Learning styles were not discussed until the 1970s)

✓ encyclopedia from 2005

✓ teachers, especially elementary level

___ commercial web site selling a learning styles inventory *(retail sites are not usually considered objective sources)*

✓ university web site discussing research into learning styles

✓ homeschooling veterans who have taught several children

✓ book or article written by researcher discussing experiments with learning styles

✓ podcast or video of an overview of learning styles

___ random opinions about learning styles on the Yahoo Answers web page

p. 207

Proofreading Exercise

...you? **Are** you...

...answered **an** obscure...

...just as ~~as~~ it...

"**But** are you...

"**But** you must...

...names," **shrieked** Inglewood...

...something," **thundered** the...

...all **its** ten **thousand** leaves

...of **the** rocking...

p. 210

Creating Interview Questions Exercise

The best questions are all open-ended. This does not mean that you cannot ask yes and no questions. You may want to follow up an open-ended question with a yes and no question. If you begin with a yes and no question, you will usually have to follow it with an open-ended question to direct the interview toward the information you need.

1. Yes
   (blank)
2. Yes
   (blank)
3. (blank)
   Yes
4. (blank)
   Yes
5. Yes
   (blank)
6. Yes
   (blank)

p. 213

Proofreading Exercise

...It **strikes** me...

...my **morning** shave.

p. 218

Poetry Comprehension Exercise

1. The poem is about praying the Rosary. The poem is about Kilmer's understanding of the meaning of praying the Rosary. **Answers may vary.**

2. This poem should be read slowly. In fact, Kilmer chose words that are difficult to say quickly. For instance, he uses long vowel sounds and many words containing "ll," "o" and "or" and "ong." We usually draw these sound combinations out slightly when speaking.

3. A lute is an ancient stringed musical instrument, intended to accompany singing.

4. Laureate means a person who has been acknowledged for achieving distinction in a specific area of arts or science, such as poetry or chemistry.

5. The "Master of all song" would be God.

p. 218
Reading Further Exercise
Answers may vary.

1. Kilmer compares prayer with music, singing, lutes, and harps.

2. In my opinion, Kilmer uses this comparison to make the reader think more deeply about how and why we pray the rosary. He wants us to take a new look at what we are doing. We are creating something beautiful and something beautifully ordered and harmonious when we mediate and pray the Rosary.

3. Kilmer refers to frustration at not being skillful enough to praise God. This frustration is resolved with the emotions of joy, or appreciation, and gratitude at the value of the Rosary which allows all to pray skillfully.

4. This poem achieved the poet's purpose of making me think about the Rosary in a new way. The Rosary is a stringed instrument that the pray-er can bring to life. With constant practice, the pray-er becomes more skilled at prayer and brings her own experiences and emotions to prayer. **Answers may vary.**

p. 222
Proofreading Exercise
There is one error, which is a comma splice.

...expanding **outward. Nevertheless,** the model...

p. 224
Series of Events Exercise
Answers may vary.

1. tripped over shoe/stumbled as dog ran past

2. saddled horse/went into barn and asked groom to saddle horse

3. bought a gift/ordered flowers

4. dog refused to get out of car/dog growled at vet

5. rocked baby/played games with baby

6. key fit locked desk drawer which contained gold coins/someone stole key because that person knew which lock the key would open

p. 225
Deciding Events Exercise
Answers will vary.

1. Science fiction
preparing for space travel
exploring/building/repairing a
    spaceship
meeting/escaping from aliens
discovering/colonizing a planet
getting lost in space

2. Journal of a Prisoner of War
being captured
experiencing emotions of fear, anger,
    frustration, hunger, solitude
treatment by guards
plans for survival or escape

3. Your Autobiography
where and when you were born
educational events
family adventures
sports, hobbies, skills
achievements and failures
hopes for the future

4. Fictional account of a shipwreck
reason for being on a ship
cause of shipwreck
salvage from the ship
location of shipwreck
adventures while adjusting to being
    shipwrecked
rescue

p. 225
Choosing the Order of Events Exercise
Answers will vary.

1. Science Fiction—I would begin this story in the middle with the discovery of a new planet to put the reader right into the emotional thrill of discovery.

2. Journal of a Prisoner of War—I would begin this story on the first day of captivity to show how the prisoner changes.

3. Your Autobiography—I would begin my autobiography at the present time and write it backwards because the events closest to the present time will be the easiest to remember in detail.

4. Fictional Account of a Shipwreck—I would begin the shipwreck at the most dangerous point when all hope seemed futile to get the reader quickly involved in the dangers and adventures of the story.

p. 226
Proofreading Exercise
...try **to** fight...
...become **too** involved...
...a **badly worded** road...
...sign, **heartbreak** among...
...of **a** slipshod...
...telegram. **Think** of...
...only **fair**.

p. 227
Listening Exercise

1. Usually one person will dominate a conversation, and that person will be the one with the most influence or power in the group.

2. Sometimes, but often not!

3. In natural conversation, the tendency is to use half-sentences and one-word answers or questions with pauses and filler words, such as ah, or um.

4. Most people do have definite speech patterns. They tend to use the same word again and again. Some people will speak precisely, others will mumble, and many people use casual language when speaking spontaneously. My tendency is not to complete my sentences. Do you know what your speech pattern is?

p. 229
Purpose of Dialogue Exercise
Answers may vary.

1. Moving the plot forward, revealing the character, providing information to the reader, engaging the reader in the action

2. Showing conflict, revealing the character, engaging the reader in the action, providing information to the reader

3. Moving the plot forward, providing information to the reader, showing conflict (to create suspense)